Reading for Better Comprehension

by
Carolyn M. Bruno, M.A.
and
Marion L. McGuire, Ph.D.

American Guidance Service, Inc.
Circle Pines, Minnesota 55014-1796

Editors:
Barbara Pokrinchak, Ph.D.
Mary D. Szarek, M.L.A.

Printed in the United States of America

ISBN 0-88671-965-8 (Previously ISBN 0-86601-665-1)

Order Number: 80420

A 0

Contents

Unit 5: Understanding Visual Aids

Lesson 1:   SETTING A PURPOSE FOR READING

> How do I set a purpose for reading?

Words to Discuss	
purpose	contribute
comprehension	alert

Did you ever ask yourself, "Why am I reading this"? The answer to this question is your *purpose* for reading. Knowing your purpose for reading is very important to your *comprehension*. When you have to read a chapter in your social studies book, stop and ask yourself, "Why am I reading this chapter?" Here are some clues:

1. Did your teacher ask you to look over the chapter so you will be able to *contribute* to a class discussion? If so, your purpose will be to find out, in general, what the chapter is about.

2. Are you going to have a test tomorrow? Your purpose will be to read carefully to make sure you remember the important facts and ideas.

3. Do you have to answer the questions at the end of the chapter? In that case, your purpose will be to gather ideas to answer the questions. You should read the questions first. Then you will be *alert* to the information you need to answer them.

Reading to contribute to a class discussion, to prepare for a test, or to answer questions at the end of a chapter requires three different purposes for reading. Knowing your purpose for reading will help you to decide how carefully you should read. It will also help you to choose the information you need to understand and remember.

Setting a purpose for reading is the first step in improving comprehension.

Unit 1: Getting Ready to Read

A. Vocabulary Development

Locate the "Words to Discuss" printed in italics in the lesson. Read each of the sentences in which one of the words appears. Try to decide what the word means in that sentence. Discuss your ideas. Look the word up, if necessary.

B. Did I Get the Message? Circle the letter in front of the correct answer.

1. What does it mean to set a purpose for reading?

   a. To know why you are reading.

   b. To know about social studies.

   c. To set a time to study.

   d. To have a class discussion.

2. How does reading for a specific purpose help you to have better comprehension?

   a. You are concentrating more on the purpose than on the reading itself.

   b. You are concentrating more on the details than you are on the main idea.

   c. You are concentrating more on the information that will answer your question.

   d. You are not concentrating on what you are reading.

C. Writing Practice: Read this example of an assignment and a purpose for reading.

Assignment: Be ready to do the experiment described in Chapter 12 of your science book.

Purpose for Reading: Read to find out what the experiment is, what materials you will need for it, and what the outcome should be.

Directions: Now write your own example. Make up an assignment that requires reading. Then write the purpose for which you would read in order to do that assignment.

Assignment: _____

_____

Purpose for Reading: _____

_____

Lesson 2: PREVIEWING THE MATERIAL

Words to Discuss	
attraction	advance
preview	selection

What is a preview?

How do I preview?

The "coming *attraction*" of a movie is made so you will want to return to see the film. It includes exciting scenes that give you the main idea and a few important details. The producer hopes you will remember what this film is about and come back to see it.

A *preview* works in reading the way the "coming attraction" works for a movie. It gives you the important ideas in *advance*. This helps you to understand and remember enough to improve your comprehension as you read.

Before you read any assignment, preview it. If it is a whole chapter in a textbook, go through it. Get an idea of what it is about. Then, go back and read the title. Read all the information in boldface type, such as subtitles and headings. Look at the pictures, charts, and graphs, and read the captions under them. If there is a summary at the end, read that, too. Think about the ideas you have gathered. Then, turn the headings into questions and read to answer your questions.

But, what if you have to read only four paragraphs? Should you still preview? Yes! Do it like this. Read the first paragraph and the first sentence of the other paragraphs quickly. Then read the last sentence of the entire *selection*. Now go back and read your assignment. Previewing will help you to create categories for storing the details you encounter as you read.

Previewing is an important step in improving comprehension, yet it does not take much time. You will find that it is the "coming attraction" of your reading.

A. Vocabulary Development

Locate the "Words to Discuss" printed in italics in the lesson. Read each of the sentences in which one of the words appears. Try to decide what the word means in that sentence. Discuss your ideas. Look the word up, if necessary.

B. **Did I Get the Point?** Circle the letter in front of the correct answer.

1. How is previewing before reading like watching the coming attractions of a movie?

   a. It makes you take the time to read the information again.

   b. It gives you the main idea and enough of the details to help you to remember more.

   c. It gives away the plot and the specific episodes.

   d. It makes you take the time to read the charts you usually skip.

2. How do you preview a chapter in a textbook?

   a. By opening the book and starting to read from the beginning.

   b. By watching the producer's preview first so you will want to return to see the movie.

   c. By quickly reading everything you need to know.

   d. By looking at the titles, headings, pictures and charts, and reading the summary before you begin the assignment.

3. How do you preview a reading selection?

   a. By reading all paragraphs in order from the beginning.

   b. By reading the first sentence of all the paragraphs in the chapter.

   c. By reading the first paragraph, the first sentence of the other paragraphs, and the last sentence of the selection.

   d. By reading the last sentence of the paragraphs that are near the end of the selection.

C. **Writing Practice:** Read this example of the use of a preview.

Assignment: Read chapter 10 in your history book. Prepare to contribute to a class discussion.

Discussion: Sarah read the chapter but feels that she does not remember enough to discuss it. She does not have time to reread. What should she do? One thing she could do is use the preview technique again as a quick review. It will refresh her memory and allow her to remember more of what she read.

Directions: Now write an assignment that can be done best by using a preview. Then discuss its advantages, as in the case above.

Assignment: _____

_____

Discussion: _____

_____

STUDENT CHECKLIST FOR UNIT 1

This checklist will enable you to decide if your reading habits help you when you are getting ready to read.

Directions: Think about the following reading habits. Then put a check mark in the first column if you already have that habit. If you do not have that habit but plan to work on it, put a check in the second column.

	I have the habit.	I will work on it.
1. Before I read, I think about why I am reading the assignment and set a purpose for reading.	_____	_____
2. Before I read, I preview to get a general idea of what the selection is about.	_____	_____
3. If a textbook chapter is long, I divide it into parts and preview each part before I read it.	_____	_____
4. When reading textbooks, I turn titles and subtitles into questions and read to answer my questions.	_____	_____
5. Depending upon my purpose for reading, I sometimes read at a slower than average pace to pay more attention to detail.	_____	_____

Unit 2: Reading for Details

Lesson 1: READING TO FOLLOW THE DETAILS OF AN EVENT

Words to Discuss		
destination	ultimately	interrupted
international	responsible	board

What are details?

Details are to the main idea of a selection as bricks are to a house. Details are the facts and ideas that explain, describe, and sometimes give importance to the main point that is made. Getting the details is often very important to your understanding of the reading selection.

In this lesson, you begin to read the story of a musical group called "Fire and Ice." Try to remember the details as you read to find out how the tour began at Heathrow Airport, London.

Departing from Heathrow Airport

Today is an important day for the British musical group, "Fire and Ice." All five members are standing at Heathrow Airport in London with airline tickets in their hands and high hopes in their hearts. Their *destination* is Kennedy Airport in New York City, where they will begin their first American tour.

The airport was crowded, and Jeremy Johns stayed near his sister, Julie, and the rest of the group. Passengers usually arrive one hour early for an *international* flight. However, since they had to check their guitars, drums, bass, and other equipment through customs, the agent told them to arrive two hours early. They also needed time to take out the fifty-thousand-dollar ($50,000) insurance policy for the equipment.

Jeremy's thoughts turned to money. It was amazing how much the tickets cost, even though they managed to get the super-saver price. "I hope this tour pays off our debts," thought Jeremy. "I should let Brian, our manager, worry about the money, but he always reminds me that I'm *ultimately responsible*."

Jeremy's thoughts were *interrupted* by the call to *board* the plane. "Flight 801 to New York. Passengers seated in rows 45 to 60, please board now," came over the loudspeaker.

A. Vocabulary Development

Locate the "Words to Discuss" printed in italics in the story. Read each of the sentences in which one of the words appears. Try to decide what the word means in that sentence. Discuss your ideas. Look the word up, if necessary.

B. Did I Get the Details? Circle the letter in front of the correct answer.

1. The musical group is on its way to

    a. New Orleans.   c. New York.

    b. New Jersey.   d. New Haven.

2. The person who is ultimately responsible for the group is

 a. Judy Johns.   c. Jimmy Johns.

 b. Brian Johns.   d. Jeremy Johns.

3. How many hours before an international flight must passengers usually arrive at the airport?

 a. One   c. Three

 b. Two   d. Four

4. How much insurance did the group take out on their equipment?

 a. $25,000   c. $75,000

 b. $50,000   d. $100,000

5. The name of the musical group is

 a. Hot as Fire.   c. Fire and Ice.

 b. Fire and Nice.   d. Fire Away.

C. Writing Practice

Here is an example of a detail question:

Where will Flight 801 land? (At Kennedy Airport in New York.)

Directions: Write three detail questions about the story and answer them.

1. Question: _____
    Answer: _____

2. Question: _____
    Answer: _____

3. Question: _____
    Answer: _____

Directions: Write the answer to the following question.

Why do you think Jeremy is worrying about money? Give as many details as you can.

_____

_____

_____

_____

Lesson 2: RECALLING DETAILS IN SEQUENCE

Words to Discuss

passenger   taxied

assigned   beverage

attendant

Is sequence important?

Details sometimes occur in a sequence or order that is important to the comprehension of what we read. Directions, steps to be taken, and events in a story should be remembered in the order in which they are given.

As you read this part of the story, think of the order in which things happened.

On the Airplane

Since the plane is boarded from back to front, the *passengers* with seats in the rear are called first. Then, the rest of the passengers are called to board according to their *assigned* seats. That meant that Dave, the drummer, and Sal, the bass player, would be getting on soon. They had seats near the middle of the plane. They smiled and waved to their families as they showed their boarding passes to the flight *attendant*. Julie and Jeremy were sitting together in the front section. Brian was there also, just across the aisle. As these three were chatting excitedly, the plane *taxied* out to the runway. Soon the pilot received the "OK" to take off, and they were in the air in no time.

This was a seven-and-a-half hour flight, so they would receive a *beverage* service and two meals, lunch and dinner. As soon as the plane leveled off, the flight attendants offered free soda, coffee, or tea to everyone. The passengers relaxed while waiting for lunch to arrive. Lunch was a cold-cut sandwich, potato salad, and cake. It wasn't bad, in Jeremy's opinion.

After lunch the passengers chose how they would like to spend the afternoon. The flight attendants rented headphones to those who wanted to watch the movie or to listen to music. When the movie began, most of the passengers quieted down. Some people decided to read or to take a nap.

A. **Vocabulary Development**

Locate the "Words to Discuss" printed in italics in the story. Read each of the sentences in which one of the words appears. Try to decide what the word means in that sentence. Discuss your ideas. Look the words up, if necessary.

B. **Did I Get the Details?** Circle the letter in front of the correct answer.

1. The three who sat near the front of the plane are

   a. Jeremy, Julie, and Dave.
   b. Jeremy and Julie.
   c. Julie, Brian, and Dave.
   d. Jeremy, Julie, and Brian.

2. How many hours does it take to fly from London to New York?

   a. Six.
   b. Six and a half.
   c. Seven.
   d. Seven and a half.

3. The headphones can be used for

   a. listening only to the music.
   b. the volume and the scenery.
   c. the movie and the music.
   d. listening to the television.

4. On an airplane, the passengers usually

   a. buy the headphones.
   b. rent the headphones.
   c. bring their own headphones.
   d. borrow the headphones.

5. An airplane boards from

   a. front to back.
   b. left to right.
   c. back to front.
   d. right to left.

C. Writing Practice

1. Some of the story details are given below, but they are not in the right sequence. On the lines provided below, write the sentences in the order in which they happened in the story.

    (a) As the plane taxied to the runway, the group was talking excitedly. (b) Lunch was served. (c) When the passengers were called for boarding, Dave and Sal said good-bye and boarded first. (d) The headphones were rented to some passengers and the movie began. (e) The passengers waited for lunch to arrive. (f) Julie, Jeremy, and Brian soon followed.

    _____

    _____

    _____

    _____

    _____

    _____

    _____

2. Pretend you are going to travel somewhere by plane. Write the directions from your home to the airport. Make sure they are in the right order.

    _____

    _____

    _____

    _____

    _____

3. Why is it sometimes necessary to remember the details of what you read

    in sequence? _____

    _____

    _____

Lesson 3: READING TO FIND DETAILS THAT EXPLAIN

How do details explain?

Words to Discuss			
descent	awe	imposing	impressive
suspension	massive	skyline	passport

Sometimes details explain by telling what, how, or why. As you read this part of the story, notice how Brian explained the difference between New York and London. Also, look for the details that explain why Jeremy was impressed by his introduction to the United States.

An Impressive Entrance to the United States

"How much longer will we be in the air?" asked Julie.

"We'll be in New York in two more hours," said Brian. "Arrival time is two-thirty in the afternoon although it will be seven-thirty in London. There is a five-hour time difference between New York and London. We'll have to set our watches back."

"Well, my stomach says it's dinner time. I'm hungry," said Julie. Turning to Jeremy, Julie asked, "Did you ask for chicken or steak, Jeremy?"

"Steak, of course," was the reply. "I never pass up a steak."

After dinner the pilot's voice came over the loudspeaker to tell the passengers that they were beginning the *descent* to Kennedy Airport. He pointed out some of the sights that could be seen from the plane. Jeremy saw the Statue of Liberty for the first time. It was breathtaking. The pilot then directed their attention to the Verrazano Bridge, the world's largest *suspension* bridge. He also told them to keep their eyes peeled for the Empire State Building and the United Nations Building. Everyone looked at these sights in *awe*. The buildings were quite *massive* and *imposing* on the *skyline* and, certainly, an *impressive* introduction to the United States. Then the plane circled around to land at John Fitzgerald Kennedy Airport.

Soon they were walking toward *passport* control and the customs area to check in before picking up their luggage and equipment.

A. **Vocabulary Development**

Locate the "Words to Discuss" printed in italics in the story. Read each of the sentences in which one of the words appears. Try to decide what the word means in that sentence. Discuss your ideas. Look the word up, if necessary.

B. **Did I Get the Details?** Circle the letter in front of the correct answer.

1. What is the time difference between New York and London?

   a. Two and one-half hours.
   b. Five hours.
   c. Seven and one-half hours.
   d. Seven hours.

2. When they land, it will be 7:30 P.M. in London. What time will it be in New York?

   a. 12:30 A.M.
   b. 1:00 P.M.

   c. 2:30 P.M.
   d. 5:00 P.M.

3. The first sight of New York was the

   a. Verrazano Bridge.
   b. Empire State Building.
   c. World Trade Center.
   d. Statue of Liberty.

4. What was the choice of meat for dinner?

   a. Chicken or turkey.
   b. Turkey or steak.

   c. Steak or chicken.
   d. Chicken or fish.

5. The Verrazano Bridge is the suspension bridge that is the world's

   a. largest.
   b. widest.

   c. most expensive.
   d. most impressive.

6. Passport control and customs must be cleared before you

   a. get off the plane.
   b. pick up your luggage.
   c. see the sights.
   d. buy American goods.

C. **Writing Practice**

1. Some of the important details are left out of the story summary below. Use words from the story to complete the sentences.

   a. Brian and Julie were discussing the _____ difference between New York and _____. Since there is a _____-hour difference, when it is 2:30 in New York, it must be _____ back home.

   b. Dinner was a choice of _____ or _____. Jeremy chose the _____.

   c. After dinner, the pilot pointed out some of the impressive _____. Jeremy saw the _____ of _____ for the first time.

   d. When the plane landed, they looked for _____ control and _____, so they could _____ in before picking up their luggage.

2. In your own words, explain what Jeremy saw as the airplane approached New York City.

   _____

   _____

   _____

   _____

   _____

   _____

3. Pretend you are traveling on an airplane to London. Describe the two choices on the menu for dinner and tell what you would choose. Include the main course, salad, dessert, and beverage. Then explain in detail why you would like this particular meal.

   _____

   _____

   _____

   _____

   _____

   _____

   _____

Lesson 4:   COMPARING DETAILS

What can be compared?

Words to Discuss		
efficient	numerous	amateur
borough	accustomed	impromptu

Things that are alike in some details and different in others can be compared. For example, we can compare two animals, two airplanes, or two vegetables. In the story below, notice the things in New York that the group finds different from London.

Arriving in Manhattan

Leaving JFK Airport, the group climbed into the motor coach that they had rented for the tour. Bernie, the driver, was very *efficient* and helpful. He seemed to know how to handle expensive musical equipment, and they were glad that he would be with them on the tour.

Now they were on their way across New York, through the *boroughs* of Queens and Brooklyn. They were surprised and impressed by the *numerous* high-rise apartment buildings, one after another, all the way into Manhattan.

Finally they reached their motel, located in midtown among the famous high-rise office buildings, fifty to one hundred stories high. It was a convenient location for both sightseeing and working.

After they checked into the hotel, although tired from their long flight, they took a walk. It was 4:00 P.M., and they wanted to get *accustomed* to New York time. Plus, it was exciting to be in the "Big Apple."

The streets of New York were quite different from those in London. The cars were driving on the "wrong" side. The taxicabs were yellow instead of black, and their drivers were yelling out of the windows at the cars going by. On the sidewalks were stands where people sold everything from cheap goods to expensive jewelry. When they walked through Greenwich Village, they saw jugglers, *amateur* musicians playing violins and guitars, and mimes putting on *impromptu* skits.

Later, they walked past the Empire State Building, whose 102 stories made it the tallest building in the world for thirty years. It has recently been surpassed by the World Trade Center, at 110 stories, and the Sears Tower in Chicago. Yes, Manhattan is an exciting city in which to begin a United States tour.

With their first concert in mind, they ate an early dinner and returned to their hotel for some rest. They wanted to be ready to perform.

A. **Vocabulary Development**

> Locate the "Words to Discuss" printed in italics in the story. Read each of the sentences in which one of the words appears. Try to decide what the word means in that sentence. Discuss your ideas. Look the word up, if necessary.

B. **Did I Get the Details?** Circle the letter in front of the correct answer.

1. What type of transportation did the group plan to use on their tour of the U.S.?

   a. Train.
   b. Motor coach.
   c. Airplane.
   d. Limousine.

2. On the way into Manhattan, they crossed the boroughs of

   a. Queens and Bronx.
   b. Brooklyn and Bronx.
   c. Queens and Manhattan.
   d. Brooklyn and Queens.

3. New York is noted for its buildings that are

   a. sky-high.
   b. skyline.
   c. high-rise.
   d. highline.

4. Another name for New York is

   a. Big Apple.
   b. Neon City.
   c. Old Broadway.
   d. Big Town.

5. The taxicabs in London are

   a. yellow.
   b. red.
   c. brown.
   d. black.

6. The World Trade Center has

   a. 100 stories.
   b. 110 stories.
   c. 120 stories.
   d. 125 stories.

C. **Writing Practice**

   1. Compare the "Fire and Ice" group with any musical group you know. Be ready to give details about how the two groups are alike and different.

	Fire and Ice	**Other Group**
Home country?	_____	_____
Number in group?	_____	_____
Number of males/females?	_____	_____
Are the members related?	_____	_____
Instruments played?	_____	_____
Other? _____	_____	_____

   2. Compare the details given about New York City with the same kinds of information about your city or town. Write the details in two lists as indicated below.

	New York City	**My Home Town**
Size?	_____	_____
Buildings?	_____	_____
Traffic?	_____	_____
Drivers?	_____	_____
Shopping?	_____	_____
Outdoor entertainers?	_____	_____
Other? _____	_____	_____

   3. Compare baseball and softball. Give as many details as you can.

     a. Baseball and softball are alike in these ways: _____

       _____

       _____

       _____

       _____

     b. Baseball and softball are different in these ways: _____

       _____

       _____

       _____

       _____

Lesson 5: MAPPING DETAILS

What is mapping?

Words to Discuss		
functioning	simultaneously	acoustics
coup	crucial	marquee

Mapping is similar to outlining, but it gives the topic and the details of a paragraph in visual form. The topic is located at the center of the map. The supporting details are written on lines that come out from the topic. A map looks something like this:

supporting detail

Topic

supporting detail

supporting detail

Read to find the details of the first concert. Think about mapping them.

The First Concert

Jeremy woke up early for three reasons. His internal time clock was still *functioning* on London time, and he was looking forward to the practice session this morning. Excitement was building for their big concert tonight, too.

"Brian pulled off quite a *coup* booking us into Madison Square Garden," he thought. This is the place where all the famous bands play. It is an enormous indoor stadium that seats 20,000 people and can hold seven major events *simultaneously*. It is the home of the New York Knicks, the city's basketball team, as well as the New York Rangers, the city's hockey team.

Gathering together, they went over to the Garden to begin the practice session. This rehearsal was *crucial* as they needed to check the *acoustics*, lighting, and staging. Julie was worried about her vocals and wanted to be sure that her voice carried in such a large stadium. Her vocals with Jeremy needed to be restaged, too. Dave and Sal tuned their instruments, and then they ran through the music. After rehearsal they returned to the hotel to rest for the big event.

Brian, worrying about the bills, had already checked on ticket sales. He was told that they were good. At fifteen dollars apiece, there would be enough profit to carry them through the tour.

Driving into the Garden that night, they saw their name on the *marquee* for the first time. Then they were on stage. The crowd of 10,000, screaming and clapping its warm American welcome, rose to its feet. "Fire and Ice" was a big hit. Their careers took off here in the "Big Apple."

A. **Vocabulary Development**

Locate the "Words to Discuss" printed in italics in the story. Read each of the sentences in which one of the words appears. Try to decide what the word means in that sentence. Discuss your ideas. Look the word up, if necessary.

B. **Did I Get the Details?** Circle the letter in front of the correct answer.

1. Jeremy's reasons for waking early were that

   a. he was tired and on a different time schedule for sleeping and eating.
   b. his body was still on London time, and his time clock said he was hungry.
   c. he was still on London time, and he was looking forward to the rehearsal and the concert.
   d. he was curious about meeting with Brian to find out about ticket sales and profits.

2. Madison Square Garden holds

   a. 10,000 people.   c. 70,000 people.
   b. 20,000 people.   d. 200,000 people.

3. The two teams that call Madison Square Garden their home are the

   a. N.Y. Knicks and N.J. Rangers.
   b. N.J. Knicks and N.Y. Rangers.
   c. N.Y. Rangers and N.Y. Knicks.
   d. N.J. Knicks and N.J. Rangers.

4. "Fire and Ice" saw their name for the first time on the

   a. marquee.   c. matinee.
   b. tickets.   d. lobby wall.

5. For their performance, the stadium was

   a. sold out.   c. one-third full.
   b. half full.   d. one-quarter full.

6. They knew they were successful when

   a. the music started.   c. they counted the people.
   b. they walked on stage.   d. the crowd liked them.

C. Writing Practice

1. The first paragraph of the selection might be outlined like this:

    Topic: Reasons Jeremy Woke Early

    Supporting Details: A. Functioning on London time
    B. Looking forward to practice
    C. Excitement building for concert

    These same ideas can also be shown by a map.

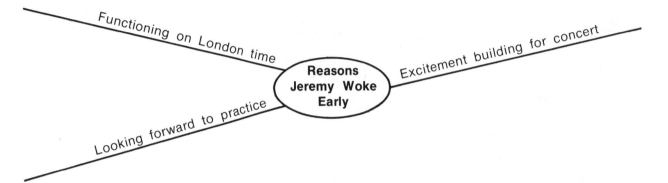

2. Now, you map the details of the second paragraph. The topic is Madison Square Garden. Find all the details the paragraph gives about Madison Square Garden. Put each one on a line coming out from the topic. Draw as many lines as you need.

Madison
Square
Garden

3. Try the third paragraph. The topic is given to you.

Things They
Did at
Rehearsal

Lesson 6: READING TO FIND REASONS

How do I find the reasons?

Words to Discuss

album	sequence	synchronizing
grueling	various	technicians

Reasons tells "why" things happen. Asking "why" as you read helps you to find the reasons, which in turn increases your understanding of actions and events.

Preview the selection to find out, in general, what the "Fire and Ice" group is doing. Then, as you read, look for reasons why the group is nervous and why the recording session took seven grueling hours.

Recording an Album

With the concert at Madison Square Garden over, the group now turned to their next big project. They were going to record an *album.* This was another "first" in their musical career, and they were all very nervous.

At the recording studio they met the producer, Steve Cuttles. He took them into the sound room to show them the tape deck controls and the microphones. This is where they would begin.

Recording an album turned out to be a *grueling* experience. Steve told them where to stand in order to sing into the microphones and where they should set up the bass and drums. Then they began to play and sing the songs they performed during last night's concert. Steve wanted the songs in the same *sequence* as in the concert because this was to be a concert album. When the sound was not clear, they had to record over again, beginning at *various* stages of a song, sometimes in the middle or near the end. This was very tricky because each time the record button was pushed, they ran the risk of accidentally erasing what was already on the tape.

Finally, after seven grueling hours, their part of the recording project was completed. Leaving the task of *synchronizing* the tape decks to Steve and the *technicians,* they returned to their hotel to pack their bags and equipment. Early the next morning they were heading north to the city of Boston to continue their concert tour.

Unit 2: *Reading for Details*

A. **Vocabulary Development**

   Locate the "Words to Discuss" printed in italics in the story.
Read each of the sentences in which one of the words appears.
Try to decide what the word means in that sentence.   Discuss
your ideas.   Look the word up, if necessary.

B. **Did I Get the Details?** Circle the letter in front of the correct answer.

   1. Recording an album was

      a. easy.
      b. exhausting.
      c. accidental.
      d. daring.

   2. The sequence of songs in the album was important because

      a. it was a history of their music.
      b. it was representative of their work.
      c. it was a concert album.
      d. it was a tricky task.

   3. When re-recording, it is possible to

      a. erase what was already on the tape.
      b. add to the size of the album.
      c. erase the musical score.
      d. erase only the music.

   4. Recording the entire album took

      a. six hours.
      b. one whole day.
      c. seven hours.
      d. seven days.

   5. Synchronizing the tape decks is usually the job of the

      a. teacher.
      b. technician.
      c. technical advisor.
      d. tutor.

C. **Writing Practice**

1. Select two of the "Words to Discuss" and write one sentence for each one. Use the same meanings as in the story. Underline the word.

    a. _____

    _____

    b. _____

    _____

2. Paragraph three of the story gives reasons why recording an album can be a grueling experience. On the lines below, list at least three reasons. Recording the album was a grueling experience because:

    a. _____

    b. _____

    c. _____

3. Now think of a task that sounds easy but, in fact, is quite difficult to do, like cooking a holiday dinner or putting a new roof on a house. Write the task on the top line. On the lines that follow, write the reasons why this task is really grueling.

    Task: _____
    Reasons why this task is grueling:

    a. _____

    _____

    b. _____

    _____

    c. _____

    _____

4. Make a map of the reasons why the task in question 3 above was a grueling experience. Insert the name of the task in the center. Then, add a line for each reason it is a grueling task.

STUDENT CHECKLIST FOR UNIT 2

This checklist will enable you to decide if your reading habits help you to read for details.

Directions: Think about the following reading habits. Then put a check mark in the first column if you already have that habit. If you do not have that habit but plan to work on it, put a check in the second column.

	I have the habit.	I will work on it.
1. When I read, I am aware of the details or facts which explain, describe, or support the main ideas or events in the story or selection.	_____	_____
2. When I read, I try to relate the details of the story or selection to the ideas or events they support.	_____	_____
3. When I read, I adjust my speed in terms of how much detail it is important to remember.	_____	_____
4. I preview before I read to create categories for storing the details I encounter as I read.	_____	_____
5. I form questions before I read to guide the search for details.	_____	_____
6. After reading, I try to summarize what I read to improve my comprehension. This helps me to remember what I read.	_____	_____

Lesson 1: FINDING THE MAIN IDEA OF A PARAGRAPH

Words to Discuss			
colonial	massacre	recreate	Parliament
conflict	stage	notorious	independent

What is the main idea?

The main idea is the overall idea of the paragraph or selection. It is a general idea that includes all of, but not more than, the details given.

Preview the selection to get the general idea of what it is about. Then, keep the title in mind as you read to find the highlights of the Boston visit.

Highlights of the Boston Visit

With Bernie driving the motor coach, they arrived in Boston in just over six hours. They were amazed at the modern super highways that stretched over such long distances. In England, this distance would have taken them across the entire country.

Boston looked very different from New York. There were some wide avenues; but they soon turned into crooked, narrow streets that were left over from *colonial* times. Bernie had some trouble maneuvering the motor coach through those narrow streets, so they decided that their tour of the city would be either on foot or by bus.

Since Boston is a city filled with a history of British and American *conflict*, this group from Britain was anxious to see where the battles took place. They took a bus to the Old State House to see where the Boston *Massacre* took place in 1770. This was the place where British troops fired on a mob of citizens. Next, they went over to the harbor where the colonists *staged* the famous Boston Tea Party in 1773. Here the Americans, in order to avoid the tax put on tea by the British, tossed the tea chests overboard. A replica of that ship is now used as a museum to *recreate* the *notorious* event. After this, *Parliament* closed the city's port:

two years later, in 1775, the Revolutionary War began. "Yes," thought Jeremy, "the Americans certainly are an *independent* people."

Their concert performance that night was at the Hatch Memorial Shell, where the Boston Symphony and the Boston Pops orchestras play. The Boston Pops is very popular in England, and the group was excited about meeting some of their members after the concert.

As it turned out, the group was just as popular here as it was in New York City. Off to a good start, the members said good-bye to the city of the bean and the cod and headed south toward Philadelphia.

A. **Vocabulary Development**

Locate the "Words to Discuss" printed in italics in the story. Read each of the sentences in which one of the words appears. Try to decide what the word means in that sentence. Discuss your ideas. Look the word up, if necessary.

B. **Did I Get the Main Idea?** Circle the letter in front of the correct answer.

1. The main idea of this story is that

    a. the group called Boston "The Home of the Bean and the Cod."
    b. Boston is six hours from New York by motor coach.
    c. Boston is noted for wide avenues and narrow streets.
    d. the group toured Boston and had a successful concert.

2. Another good title for this story is

    a. "Fire and Ice" Visits Boston.
    b. "Fire and Ice" Tours the City of Boston.
    c. "Fire and Ice" Gives a Concert in Boston.
    d. "Fire and Ice" Travels to Boston.

3. The main idea of the second paragraph is that

    a. Bernie had trouble maneuvering the motor coach.
    b. the streets of Boston are as crooked and narrow as in colonial times.
    c. Boston streets are narrow for a motor coach, so they toured on foot and by bus.
    d. the group decided to tour the city of Boston on foot or by bus.

4. The main idea of the third paragraph is that

    a. Jeremy thought Americans are certainly an independent people.
    b. the group wanted to see the places where American/British conflicts occurred.

    c. the group visited the place where the Boston Massacre occurred in 1770.

    d. the group saw the replica of the Boston Tea Party ship.

5. The main idea of the last paragraph is that

    a. the group left Boston and headed for Philadelphia.

    b. the group was popular with their concert audience in Boston.

    c. the "Fire and Ice" group was off to a good start on their tour.

    d. after another successful concert, they left for Philadelphia.

C. Writing Practice

1. Select two of the "Words to Discuss" and write one sentence for each one. Use the same meanings as in the story. Underline the word.

    a. _____

       _____

    b. _____

       _____

2. Read paragraphs 1 and 4 of the story again. Then, for each paragraph, write one sentence that tells the main idea of that paragraph.

    Paragraph 1: _____

    _____

    Paragraph 4: _____

    _____

3. Write a brief paragraph telling what happened in the years 1770, 1773, and 1775 that interested the "Fire and Ice" group. Give the paragraph a good title that tells what it is about.

    Title: _____

    _____

    _____

    _____

    _____

    _____

    _____

Lesson 2: FINDING THE MAIN IDEA OF A SELECTION

How can I find the main idea?

Words to Discuss

grid	cuing
sect	sub

The main idea of a selection is an idea that includes the main idea of each paragraph. Clues to the main idea can be found in the title and in the introductory and summary paragraphs. Look for a general idea that the selection explains or describes.

Preview this part of the story to get a general idea of the group's tour in the city of Philadelphia. Then, read to see how the title includes the main points made in the paragraphs.

Philadelphia: Another Success Story

The motor coach entered Philadelphia. This city was founded by William Penn, who laid out the city streets in a *grid* system, directly north-south or east-west. Also, there is a park in each quarter of the city. This was the first city in the United States to benefit from "city planning."

William Penn called his city "Philadelphia," meaning *brotherly love* in Greek. Philadelphia has been nicknamed the "City of Brotherly Love." Pennsylvania was the first colony to allow freedom of worship for all *sects*. Penn also guaranteed every taxpayer the right to vote, every prisoner the right to be heard, and every man a trial by jury.

There were two things about Philly that interested Jeremy and his friends: its colonial history and the music of the 60's. It was here that the American colonists met to break with England. British troops occupied Philadelphia in 1777. Julie wanted to see Independence Hall, where the Declaration of Independence and the Constitution were signed. Sal wanted to see the Liberty Bell. They all felt they were really a part of the history of long ago.

As for the music of the 60's, there was nothing like it. Dick Clark and the American Bandstand were on TV every day. The musical greats like Chubby Checker, Little Richard, and the Everly Brothers appeared on his show. The Beatles' records were played all of the time. Jeremy especially liked hearing them. He had quite a collection of Beatles' music. The "Fire and Ice" group was not as well known as the musical greats yet, but they were working on it.

When it was time to prepare for the concert, the stage manager assisted Brian with the lighting and *cuing* for their songs. There was no time left for dinner, so one of the stage hands brought in some of the famous Philly *subs*. These sandwiches are called heroes or poorboys in other parts of the country.

The concert was both exciting and draining. Yet the crowd applauding their every song and the "groupies" hanging around the theater for autographs left them with fond memories. The tour was in full swing, and Washington, D.C., was waiting for them.

A. **Vocabulary Development**

Locate the "Words to Discuss" printed in italics in the story. Read each of the sentences in which one of the words appears. Try to decide what the word means in that sentence. Discuss your ideas. Look the word up, if necessary.

B. **Did I Get the Main Idea?** Circle the letter in front of the correct answer.

1. The main idea of this story is that

    a. people were very welcoming to the group in Philadelphia.
    b. Philadelphia is the city of brotherly love.
    c. the group enjoyed the attractions and the people of Philadelphia.
    d. Philadelphia is famous for its steak sandwiches and Philly subs.

2. Another good title for this story is

    a. The Attractions of Philly.   c. Philadelphia, a Planned City.
    b. The Concert Tour in Philly.   d. City of Brotherly Love.

3. The main idea of the first paragraph is that

    a. Philadelphia was the first planned city.
    b. Philadelphia streets are laid out in a grid shape.
    c. the main streets run north-south.
    d. Philadelphia was founded by William Penn.

4. The main idea of the second paragraph is that

    a. Philadelphia means "The City of Brotherly Love."
    b. the first free colony made taxpayers happy.
    c. taxpayers should have a right to vote.
    d. a prisoner has a right to be heard.

5. The main idea of the last paragraph is that

    a. Philly gave them a warm welcome.
    b. the concert crowd was large.
    c. the crowd applauded their approval.
    d. they left Philly tired but happy.

Unit 3: The Main Idea

C. Writing Practice

1. Select two of the "Words to Discuss" and write one sentence for each one. Use the same meanings as in the story. Underline the word.

   a. _____

   _____

   b. _____

   _____

2. Read paragraph 3 about the historical sites in Philly. Write one sentence that contains the main idea of the paragraph.

   _____

   _____

3. Read paragraph 4 about the music of the 60's. Write one sentence that contains the main idea of the paragraph.

   _____

   _____

4. Write the main idea of each paragraph in the spaces provided below. You may look back at your answers to earlier questions for help.

   Paragraph 1: _____

   _____

   Paragraph 2: _____

   _____

   Paragraph 3: _____

   _____

   Paragraph 4: _____

   _____

   Paragraph 5: _____

   _____

   Last paragraph: _____

   _____

5. Now write a sentence that gives the main idea of the selection. It should be general enough to include the main idea of each paragraph which you have written above.

   _____

   _____

   _____

Lesson 3: USING THE MAIN IDEA TO WRITE A SUMMARY

Words to Discuss		
capital	striking	complex
monument	Capitol	go-go

How can I write a summary?

Once you know the main idea of each paragraph, it is not too difficult to write a summary of a selection. Just put your main idea sentences together in a paragraph. This will give you a summary of the selection.

Preview the following selection to get a quick idea of what happened in Washington, D.C. Then read the story to get more information about these events.

An Exciting Stop in the Nation's Capital

Washington, D.C., is just a short hop from Philadelphia: a two-hour ride in a motor coach. The nation's *capital* is a beautiful city filled with flowering cherry trees and *monuments*. It is a leading tourist spot in the United States. Jeremy and Julie had read in their history books in England about Washington, D.C. It was described as one of the most beautiful cities in the world. The Mall is especially *striking* with the Washington Monument at one end and the *Capitol* at the other end. Between them are gardens, fountains, and museums.

Sal and Dave said they felt badly about the War of 1812. They knew that their British forefathers had burned most of the public buildings, including the White House. When the President's house was rebuilt, it was painted white; and that is how it got the name "White House."

Brian informed them that their concert would be held in the Capital Centre, a huge entertainment *complex* seating 18,000 people and located just across the city's boundary in Largo, Maryland. Brian also told them that the seats were almost sold out.

When they arrived at the Centre to set up for their concert, the stage manager asked them if they knew about the revival of *go-go* music in the Washington area. (Go-go is a name taken from the French term *à go-go*, meaning "to your heart's content.") Brian indicated that they had heard about it but had never had the opportunity to listen to any of it.

"Well, after your concert tonight, I'll take you to Georgetown to hear some go-go music," he said. "It is a type of rock and roll that has a strong beat, with lyrics that emphasize that beat."

The evening sped by. Their concert was a hit, and the go-go music both exciting and different. This American tour was providing such wonderful opportunities to meet new people and share new music. It was exhausting but thrilling!

Unit 3: The Main Idea

A. **Vocabulary Development**

Locate the "Words to Discuss" printed in italics in the story. Read each of the sentences in which one of the words appears. Try to decide what the word means in that sentence. Discuss your ideas. Look the word up, if necessary.

B. **Did I Get the Main Idea?** Circle the letter in front of the correct answer.

1. The main idea of this story is that

   a. D.C. is the home of the Capital Centre.
   b. D.C. lived up to its reputation as a beautiful city.
   c. the revival of go-go music took place in the D.C. area.
   d. D.C. offered "Fire and Ice" many different experiences.

2. Another good title for this story is

   a. How the White House Got Its Name.
   b. The Music and Sights of Washington.
   c. The Washington Monument.
   d. The Cherry-Blossom City.

3. The main idea of the first paragraph is that

   a. D.C. lived up to its reputation as a beautiful city.
   b. Julie and Jeremy read about D.C. in their history books.
   c. there are beautiful monuments and gardens in D.C.
   d. D.C. is one of the leading tourist spots in the nation.

4. The main idea of the second paragraph is that

   a. Sal and Dave felt remorse about the British burning of Washington during the War of 1812.
   b. the group, expecting a large crowd, set up for their concert in the Capital Centre.
   c. the White House, burned by the British along with other buildings in 1812, was rebuilt and given its name.
   d. Washington is a city of flowering trees, gardens, and beautiful buildings—a treasure house for its many tourists.

5. The main idea of the 4th and 5th paragraphs combined is that

   a. the group went sightseeing in Georgetown after the concert.
   b. the group set up for their concert in the Capital Centre.
   c. go-go is a name taken from the French term à go-go.
   d. the group had the opportunity to hear go-go music in Georgetown.

C. **Writing Practice**

1. Select two of the "Words to Discuss" and write one sentence for each one. Use the same meanings as in the story. Underline the word.

    a. _____

    _____

    b. _____

    _____

2. Reread the first paragraph of this lesson, "How can I write a summary?" Then write a summary of the story by putting your main idea statements together in one paragraph. You may look back at your answers to earlier questions for help.

    Summary of: **An Exciting Stop in the Nation's Capital**

    _____

    _____

    _____

    _____

    _____

    _____

    _____

    _____

    _____

    _____

    _____

    _____

    _____

    _____

    _____

    _____

Lesson 4: THE TOPIC AND THE MAIN IDEA

Words to Discuss		
basking	capacity	encore
reputation	receptive	theme

What is a topic?

The topic is the subject that is discussed in a paragraph or longer selection. The main idea answers the question, "What, in general, does the author tell me about the topic?"

Preview the following selection to get the main ideas. Then read the selection to see how each paragraph tells something about the title, or topic.

"Fire and Ice" at Fort Lauderdale

The group was happy to be arriving in Fort Lauderdale, Florida. They relished their first view of palm trees and enjoyed the warm temperatures. Here they were looking forward to swimming and *basking* in the sun. The beaches in England were so different because of the cool weather. At the famous English resort, Brighton Beach, it is usually too cold to go into the water.

Joining the crowd of 50,000 students who were visiting Fort Lauderdale on their holiday break provided a good opportunity for "Fire and Ice," too. The group knew that the young people were the ones who bought records, and who could make them famous. It was fortunate that "Fire and Ice" could play their music and sing their songs to the throng of students here at this time.

They would be performing at War Memorial Auditorium in Holiday Park. It is a very modern auditorium that draws large crowds. When the last group performed here, tickets sold for $10.00 apiece. Since "Fire and Ice" was only beginning to make a name for itself, tickets were $7.00. That was still a reasonable admission price as it would give Brian and the group enough profit to pay their expenses. They had done well in the larger cities up North, and their *reputation* was spreading.

The group was very popular with the students who filled the auditorium to *capacity*. The crowd was *receptive* to their music, applauding loudly and bringing "Fire and Ice" back to the stage twice for *encores*. The group played their *theme* song again, elated about being called back to the stage.

They were now ready to relax on the beach for a few days. They would enjoy Florida's sun, sand, and surf before leaving for the next part of their tour.

A. **Vocabulary Development**

Locate the "Words to Discuss" printed in italics in the story. Read each of the sentences in which one of the words appears. Try to decide what the word means in that sentence. Discuss your ideas. Look the word up, if necessary.

B. **Did I Get the Main Idea?** Circle the letter in front of the correct answer.

1. The main idea of this story is that

   a. Fort Lauderdale provided opportunities for success and relaxation.

   b. Fort Lauderdale's beaches are different from Brighton Beach in England.

   c. students visiting Fort Lauderdale crowd the beaches during college breaks.

   d. Fort Lauderdale and the War Memorial Auditorium hold pleasant memories for the group.

2. Another good title for this story is "Fort Lauderdale:

   a. Home of the Palm Tree."   c. Beaches, Students, and Music."

   b. Rest and Relaxation."   d. The Students and the Music."

3. The main idea of the first paragraph is that

   a. because England is rainy, the beaches are in the resort area in Brighton.

   b. England's beaches are warm and sunny, especially in the summer.

   c. the group was looking forward to Florida's sunny weather and palm trees.

   d. because of England's cool climate, the group was looking forward to Florida's sun.

4. The main idea of the second paragraph is that

   a. fifty thousand students were on a holiday break at Fort Lauderdale.

   b. the young people of America are the ones who buy records.

   c. the group had a chance to perform for the young people who buy records.

   d. many students who join the group in Fort Lauderdale become famous.

5. The main idea of the third paragraph is that

   a. when famous groups perform, tickets are sold for $10.00 apiece.

   b. the "Fire and Ice" group is beginning to make a name for itself.

   c. although tickets were reasonably priced, the profits paid the group's expenses and their reputation was spreading.

   d. the group performed at the War Memorial Auditorium, which is a modern auditorium in Holiday Park, located in Fort Lauderdale.

C. Writing Practice

1. Select two of the "Words to Discuss" and write one sentence for each one. Use the same meanings as in the story. Underline the word.

    a. _____

    _____

    b. _____

    _____

2. Reread the answer to "What is a topic?" at the beginning of this lesson. Then write a main idea statement for each paragraph. Refer to Part B, 3 through 5, for your first three statements. In the second column, choose some key words from the main idea statement to form a topic. The first one is done for you.

	Main Idea of Paragraph	Topic
1.	*Because of England's cool climate, the group was looking forward to Florida's sun.*	*Florida's Sun, a Welcome Change*
2.	_____	_____
	_____	_____
3.	_____	_____
	_____	_____
4.	_____	_____
	_____	_____
5.	_____	_____
	_____	_____

3. Now do the same thing for the main idea of the entire story. See Part B1, page 39, for the main idea statement you chose.

Main Idea of the Story	Topic
_____	_____
_____	_____
_____	_____

Lesson 5:   INDEPENDENT SUMMARY WRITING

Words to Discuss		
deter	trolley	Creole
impact	hearty	specialty

Review of summary writing

Write a main idea statement for each paragraph. Put them together in paragraph form. This is your summary. If the topic is not stated, use key words from the main idea of the whole selection to form one. If the selection has a title, you may use that.

Preview the selection to get a general idea of the group's experiences in New Orleans. Then read this part of the story. Look for main ideas to use in writing a summary.

Memorable Moments in New Orleans

The next stop on the tour was New Orleans, Louisiana, home of jazz! The group "Fire and Ice" could talk of nothing else on their way there. It would be exciting to experience a type of music that originated in America as far back as the 1890's.

When they arrived, they headed straight for Preservation Hall in the French Quarter, where jazz in its truest form is played. The hall was jammed with people. It was "standing room only." Even this did not *deter* the group from staying for hours to listen to the jazz band perform. Afterward, Brian introduced himself to the musicians and told them of their own engagement to play. The group talked into the night about music and its *impact* on their lives.

The next morning they decided to take the St. Charles Avenue streetcar to tour the city. This is the city's last *trolley* line. Julie and Jeremy got off at the Garden District to see the old mansions, while Sal, Dave, and Brian went to the Tulane University campus to see the stadium where college football is played. Then they met back at the French Quarter for a lunch of *hearty* gumbo soup, a hot and spicy *Creole specialty.*

That night the group was to play at the Louisiana Superdome, where the Sugar Bowl game is played every New Year's Day. The Superdome is one of the largest indoor stadiums in the U.S. and seats 100,000 people. The group was impressed.

Arriving early to set up and rehearse, Brian inquired how ticket sales were doing. When he had called from Florida a week ago, he was told that 11,000 seats had been sold. Now he found that 6,000 more seats had been sold. Warmed by the good news, "Fire and Ice" rehearsed their songs, changing the sequence to appeal to the crowd in this city.

The group worked hard, their musical reputation was good, and they did not take their public for granted—important factors in their continuing success. It also helped that the people of New Orleans appreciated other music, as well as jazz.

A. Vocabulary Development

Locate the "Words to Discuss" printed in italics in the story. Read each of the sentences in which one of the words appears. Try to decide what the word means in that sentence. Discuss your ideas. Look the word up, if necessary.

B. Did I Get the Main Idea? Circle the letter in front of the correct answer.

1. The main idea of this story is that

   a. New Orleans is the home of jazz.

   b. New Orleans has a number of attractions.

   c. New Orleans, a city of many attractions, also appreciates different kinds of music.

   d. the "Fire and Ice" group spent a day touring New Orleans on the St. Charles Avenue streetcar.

2. The main idea of paragraph 1 is that

   a. the group talked about only one thing all the way to New Orleans.

   b. New Orleans is most famous as the Home of Jazz.

   c. "Fire and Ice" was looking forward to hearing jazz.

   d. "Fire and Ice" became excited about their experiences.

3. The main idea of paragraph 2 is that

   a. jazz is a way of life in New Orleans.

   b. "Fire and Ice" meets a jazz band in the French Quarter.

   c. the impact of music is higher when there is standing room only.

   d. the group listens to jazz and meets a jazz band.

4. The main idea of paragraph 3 is that

   a. New Orleans, a convention city, has many activities for tourists.

   b. the St. Charles Avenue streetcar is the last trolley line in New Orleans.

   c. members of the group wanted to see different sights on their tour of New Orleans.

   d. after touring along the trolley line, the group met for lunch.

5. The main idea of paragraph 4 is that

    a. the Sugar Bowl game is played at the Superdome every New Year's Day.

    b. the concert was held at an impressive stadium.

    c. the Superdome is one of the largest stadiums in Louisiana.

    d. the Superdome is a stadium with 100,000 seats.

C. Writing Practice

1. Select two of the "Words to Discuss" and write one sentence for each one. Use the same meanings as in the story. Underline the word.

    a. _____

       _____

    b. _____

       _____

2. Reread the Review of Summary Writing at the beginning of this lesson. Then, write a summary on the lines below. Follow the procedure for summary writing that you just read.

       Topic: _____

_____

_____

_____

_____

_____

_____

_____

_____

_____

_____

_____

_____

_____

_____

STUDENT CHECKLIST FOR UNIT 3

This checklist will enable you to decide if your reading habits help you in finding the main idea.

Directions: Think about the following reading habits. Then put a check mark in the first column if you already have that habit. If you do not have that habit but plan to work on it, put a check in the second column.

	I have the habit.	I will work on it.
1. When I am looking for the main idea, I look for the overall idea of what the selection is about.	_____	_____
2. I use the title or topic to help me find the main idea of a selection.	_____	_____
3. I keep in mind that additional clues to the main idea can be found in the introduction and in the summary paragraph.	_____	_____
4. When I state my purpose for reading, I include the main idea.	_____	_____
5. To find the main idea, I look for a general idea that is explained or supported by the details.	_____	_____
6. After I read a selection, I try to state the main idea.	_____	_____
7. After I read a selection, I try to summarize what I read.	_____	_____
8. To find the topic, I look for key words in the main idea statement.	_____	_____

Lesson 1: MAKING INFERENCES

Words to Discuss		
rhinestone	interview	influence
variety	publicity	devoted

What is inference?

Inference is the process of looking at the facts or the details given and coming up with a reasonable explanation or conclusion. For example, you can infer how people feel by their voices and facial expressions. In reading, the clues are the facts and events in the story or the selection. From experience we know what will probably happen. That is inference.

Preview the selection to get a general idea of it. Then read it to find out how the group probably felt about being in Nashville.

"Fire and Ice" in "Music City, USA"

Rhinestone cowboys and musicians wearing sequined shirts and playing guitars: this is the picture most people have of "Music City, USA," or "The Country Music Capital of the World," as Nashville is called. "Fire and Ice" was looking forward to a new musical experience in the city where country music originated.

The music industry in Nashville is a $300 million business. The Grand Ole Opry, the country's longest running radio program, began in 1925. It has now moved to an auditorium in Opryland, USA, a multimillion-dollar complex. The music performed there includes country, bluegrass, Broadway, gospel, rock and roll, and other kinds as well. Also, more than half of all single records produced in the United States come out of Nashville. Have you listened to a record today? There is a 50 percent chance that it was recorded in Nashville.

"Nashville Now" is a musical *variety* and *interview* show, broadcast live from Opryland. As *publicity* for the concert,

"Fire and Ice" was invited to be on the show. When they arrived, the host shared some of the questions they would be asked so that they would not be too nervous. Jeremy and Brian answered most of them. Julie was too excited to speak, and Sal and Dave were more interested in playing music than talking about it. Then, too, it is difficult for a musical group to talk about itself. You never really know your *influence* on the public until you actually become a hit. Few groups get to that point. That was why the questions were hard to answer. However, they wanted this interview and hoped to attract a large crowd for their concert.

The concert was to be held at Opryland, USA, on its main stage. There was quite a large auditorium to fill. Still, they need not have worried; their concert was sold out. Nashville is a city *devoted* to music.

A. Vocabulary Development

Locate the "Words to Discuss" printed in italics in the story. Read each of the sentences in which one of the words appears. Try to decide what the word means in that sentence. Discuss your ideas. Look the word up, if necessary.

B. Are My Inferences Reasonable? Circle the letter in front of the correct answer.

1. From their desire to do well on the interview show, we can conclude that the group

   a. was very popular.   c. was not too popular.

   b. wanted to be more popular. d. took their popularity lightly.

2. The host of the show

   a. tried to put them at ease.   c. did not know enough about them.

   b. did not care how they felt. d. was nervous about the questions.

3. Jeremy and Brian seemed to be

   a. more concerned about succeeding than the rest of the group.

   b. not very interested in country music.

   c. too confident of the group's success.

   d. the spokesmen for the group.

4. Nashville is called the music capital of the world because

   a. all the best music comes from there.

   b. it is the home of country, bluegrass, and gospel music.

   c. 50 percent of the records are produced there.

   d. it supports and encourages many types of music.

5. If you listened to a record today, the chance that it was produced in Nashville is

    a. 3 out of 4.   c. 3 out of 5.

    b. 1 out of 2.   d. 2 out of 3.

C. Writing Practice

1. Select two of the "Words to Discuss" and write one sentence for each one. Use the same meanings as in the story. Underline the word.

    a. _____

       _____

    b. _____

       _____

2. Follow the procedure you have learned (see page 41) for writing a summary. Your summary paragraph should have four sentences, one for each paragraph in the story. Write your own topic.

    _____

    _____

    _____

    _____

    _____

    _____

    _____

3. Reread the first paragraph of the story. As you do, think how the members of the "Fire and Ice" group probably felt. Remember that Sal plays the bass and Dave, the drums. Julie and Jeremy play guitars and do vocals. Brian is the manager. Choose one member of the group. Put yourself into that person's "shoes," and tell how you think he or she felt during the interview and why you think so. You will be making inferences.

    _____

    _____

    _____

    _____

    _____

    _____

Lesson 2: MATCHING INFERENCE CLUES TO EXPERIENCE

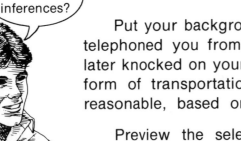

Words to Discuss		
pavilion	financial	courtyard
vivacious	skyscraper	vow

How can I make inferences?

Put your background of experience to work. If someone telephoned you from five miles away and then ten minutes later knocked on your door, you would infer that he had some form of transportation other than walking. Inferences are reasonable, based on your experience.

Preview the selection to get the sequence of events. Then, read for more detail about each event.

Chicago, Illinois: A Tour, a Cow, and a New Friend

The motor coach came by the Dan Ryan Expressway into the center of Chicago. Since the members of the group wanted to get settled, they drove directly to the University of Illinois at Chicago where they would be staying.

Bernie, the driver, had a sister Karen who was attending the University. She met them at the dorm and offered to show them the *pavilion* where they would be playing later that night. Karen, *vivacious* and lots of fun, was enjoyable company. She told them the story of Mrs. O'Leary's cow. It seems that the great fire of 1871 was started when Mrs. O'Leary's cow knocked over a lantern in the barn. No one knows if this story is true, but a fire did destroy almost the entire city of Chicago.

Then, while the others in the group rested, Karen and Sal did a bit of sightseeing. Downtown, they saw the Sears Tower, 1454 feet high, the world's tallest building. In the *financial* district they saw the Root's Rookery Building, the oldest steel-skeleton *skyscraper* in the world. Sal also wanted to see its inner *courtyard* designed by Frank Lloyd Wright, the famous architect. Then it was time to get back to the pavilion for the rehearsal.

The pavilion had good acoustics, which made their preparation easier. Several students came to help them set up. Among them was Vince, who had been at their concert at Fort Lauderdale. Pleased to have such a loyal fan, Jeremy invited him backstage after the concert.

After another hit concert, they invited Vince and several other students to join them for dinner. Karen sat between Sal and Bernie, whom she had not seen for a long time, and chatted happily with her brother and her new friend.

The group was sad to leave Chicago, especially Sal; but they *vowed* to return at some later time.

A. **Vocabulary Development**

Locate the "Words to Discuss" printed in italics in the story. Read each of the sentences in which one of the words appears. Try to decide what the word means in that sentence. Discuss your ideas. Look the word up, if necessary.

B. **Are My Inferences Reasonable?** Circle the letter in front of the correct answer.

1. We can conclude that the group's visit to Chicago was

   a. successful.
   b. relaxing.
   c. uneventful.
   d. vivacious.

2. The group of people who seemed most influenced by this concert were

   a. architects.
   b. tourists.
   c. students.
   d. drivers.

3. We can infer that, after Chicago was destroyed by fire,

   a. the people moved to another city.
   b. cows were banned within the city limits.
   c. the buildings were rebuilt.
   d. more fire stations were built.

4. Karen's relationship with her brother seemed to be

   a. loving.
   b. abrasive.
   c. overprotective.
   d. helpful.

5. The group seemed to

   a. wish they were students again.
   b. enjoy the company of different people.
   c. like traveling in a motor coach.
   d. delight in hearing local legends.

C. **Writing Practice**

1. Select two of the "Words to Discuss" and write one sentence for each one. Use the same meanings as in the story. Underline the word.

    a. _____

    _____

    b. _____

    _____

2. Based on Karen's story of Mrs. O'Leary's cow, other things you have read, and movies you have seen, what can you reasonably infer about the city of Chicago in 1871? Describe the city as you think it might have been just before the fire.

    _____

    _____

    _____

    _____

    _____

    _____

    _____

    _____

    _____

    _____

3. Read again about the student named Vince in paragraph 4. Then write a reasonable explanation of how Vince could have been at the Fort Lauderdale concert while he was a student at the University of Illinois at Chicago. You may refer back to Unit 3, Lesson 4, for information about Fort Lauderdale.

    _____

    _____

    _____

    _____

    _____

    _____

    _____

Lesson 3: INFERRING RELATIONSHIPS

Words to Discuss		
archway	attraction	invention
soar	exposition	accommodate

What is an analogy?

An analogy consists of two pairs of words or ideas related in the same way. For example, **dog** is to **bark** as **cat** is to _____. We see that the first relationship is between an animal and the noise it makes. Therefore, we should fill the blank with the noise a cat makes. (**meow**) There are innumerable ways in which words can be related. Some analogies require strong inferencing skills.

Preview this part of the story to get an overview of it. Then, as you read, look for things and events in St. Louis that are analogous to those in other cities.

St. Louis, Missouri: Where the West Begins

As the group entered the city, they could see the golden *archway*, the "Gateway to the West," as it is called. This is the Gateway Arch that *soars* above the riverfront and announces that you have reached St. Louis.

To get there, they had to cross the mighty Mississippi, one of the largest rivers in the world. The motor coach then traveled on the Daniel Boone Expressway into the downtown area. Brian thought it was great just to be on a road named after Daniel Boone. This was the group's first brush with the western part of the United States, and it held a special *attraction* for them.

How is the western part of our country different from the East? One difference is the distance between cities. For example, from St. Louis to Denver, the closest big city to the west, it is almost 1,000 miles. The large cities are much closer in the East. New York is less than 100 miles from Philadelphia, and Philadelphia only a little more than that from Washington, D.C. The West has much more open space.

In 1904, the one hundredth anniversary of the Louisiana Purchase, the Louisiana Purchase *Exposition* was held in St. Louis. Whenever you eat an ice cream cone or a hot dog or drink a glass of iced tea, you should think of this event, for these *inventions* were introduced to the world at that time. These treats are still very important to Americans. Members of the "Fire and Ice" group showed that they can be important to some of the British, too.

"Fire and Ice" played at the Palace Music Hall at the park called Six Flags Over Mid-America. This park was set up to *accommodate* groups of entertainers; it drew large crowds due to the rides and other attractions. After the concert the group went on all the rides, a new and exciting experience for them in America.

Unit 4: Inference

A. **Vocabulary Development**

Locate the "Words to Discuss" printed in italics in the story. Read each of the sentences in which one of the words appears. Try to decide what the word means in that sentence. Discuss your ideas. Look the word up, if necessary.

B. **Are My Inferences Reasonable?** Circle the letter in front of the correct answer.

1. This story is mainly about

   a. going to the Louisiana Purchase Exposition.
   b. the concert at the Six-Flags Over Mid-America park.
   c. entering the western part of the United States.
   d. the group's introduction to St. Louis.

2. We can conclude the "Fire and Ice" group was

   a. attracted by the western part of the U.S.
   b. surprised by the size of the Mississippi.
   c. distracted by the history of St. Louis.
   d. excited about riding a roller coaster.

3. We can conclude that the ice cream cone

   a. put St. Louis, Missouri, on the map.
   b. made the list of the ten most useful inventions.
   c. is a useful and delicious invention.
   d. is not available in London, England.

4. The Palace Music Hall is

   a. an amusement park.   c. an elegant theater.
   b. a western saloon.   d. a concert hall.

5. The cities in the western part of the U.S. are _____ than in the East.

   a. larger   c. more crowded
   b. farther apart   d. closer together

6. When "Fire and Ice" members think of their joyful times in St. Louis, they will most likely include

   a. riding on the Daniel Boone Expressway.
   b. crossing the mighty Mississippi River.
   c. going on the rides in the park.
   d. walking beneath the Gateway Arch.

C. **Writing Practice**

1. Select two of the "Words to Discuss" and write one sentence for each one. Use the same meanings as in the story. Underline the word.

   a. _____

   _____

   b. _____

   _____

2. Read paragraph 4 of the story. Pay particular attention to the last sentence. Then write a paragraph telling what that last sentence means to you. What do you *infer*, based on what is said? Use your background of experiences to help you decide what "Fire and Ice" probably did.

   _____

   _____

   _____

   _____

3. Review the answer to "What is an analogy?" at the beginning of this lesson. Remember that the relationship between the two words can be any kind of connection or association. Try this: **Broom** is to **sweep** as **saw** is to _____. The relationship is between a tool and its function. What do we do with a saw? (**cut**)

   You read to find things and events in St. Louis that are analogous to those in other cities. Complete the following analogies based on your reading.

   a. The ice cream cone is to St. Louis as gumbo soup is to

   _____.

   b. The Gateway Arch is to St. Louis as the Washington Monument is to _____.

   c. The hot dog is to St. Louis as the Philly sub is to

   _____.

   Here are some analogous relationships from other cities. Can you add some to the list?

   d. JFK Airport is to New York as Heathrow Airport is to

   _____.

   e. The World Trade Center is to New York as the Sears Tower is to _____.

   f. _____

   g. _____

Lesson 4: USING DETAILS TO MAKE INFERENCES

Words to Discuss		
concentric	snatch	rustling
consult	shred	boast

Are details important in inference?

Yes. All related details are important in inference. For example, if you heard a student say he found his **recorder**, you might think he found his tape recorder or VCR. But, if then he said he could not find his fipple mouthpiece (and you knew what that was), you would know that he was talking about an end-blown flute. To make correct inferences, you must **have** and **understand** all important details.

Preview this selection to get an overview of the group's activities. Then read to fill in the details.

Dallas, Texas: They Grow 'Em Big in Texas

Cowboy boots and ten-gallon hats worn by men in business suits! That is how people dress in Dallas. It is the dressiest city, the fashion center, of the West. However, they do not let you forget that it is the West.

Dallas developed in the 1930's when oil was discovered; people moved there to find their fortunes. The city grew in *concentric* circles; the roads formed a design like a spider web, making the streets hard to find. Since "Fire and Ice" was headed for their first rodeo, they did not want to be late. Bernie *consulted* a map and soon had them on the way to Grand Prairie. There they looked for Traders Village.

The rodeo arena was large, hot, and dusty. It was exactly the way Jeremy pictured it in his mind. Many cowboys were walking around with spurs on their boots and silver buckles on their belts. The air was filled with excitement. One after another, cowboys were thrown from the bulls they were

trying to ride. A few were almost stepped on, only to be saved at the last moment by a rider on horseback whose job it was to *snatch* the poor cowboy from the feet of the bull. Julie could hardly stand to watch for fear that something terrible would happen.

After watching all the *rustling* and riding, the group was hungry for their first taste of barbecue. Some stands in Traders Village sold barbecue, real western style, made with sliced meat, not *shredded*, in a red, hot sauce. Jeremy, Sal, Dave, and Bernie thought it was delicious. Julie and Brian said that it was too hot, but they ate it anyway.

Then they were back in the motor coach and headed for the amusement park, Six Flags Over Texas. The group was playing there in a large auditorium called the Music Mill. Their audience that night was one of the largest so far. The Texans *boast* that everything is bigger in Texas. They are right!

A. **Vocabulary Development**

Locate the "Words to Discuss" printed in italics in the story. Read each of the sentences in which one of the words appears. Try to decide what the word means in that sentence. Discuss your ideas. Look the word up, if necessary.

B. **Are My Inferences Reasonable?** Circle the letter in front of the correct answer.

1. Riding in a rodeo is

   a. hard on the bulls.   c. a dude ranch activity.

   b. risky to the riders.   d. tiring for visitors.

2. We can conclude that Texans are

   a. boastful people.   c. proud of Texas.

   b. fanciful dressers.   d. in the oil business.

3. This passage is mainly about

   a. the group's trip to Dallas.

   b. the group's activities in Dallas.

   c. the Capital Center at Dallas.

   d. the evening concert at Dallas.

4. Men in Texas wear cowboy boots and hats because

   a. it is dusty and sunny there.

   b. they are symbols of the West.

   c. they like to be well-dressed.

   d. it makes them feel important.

5. Dallas grew because of its

   a. high-fashion clothes.

   b. wild West rodeos.

   c. many oil wells.

   d. amusement parks.

6. Most people would think that Dallas is

   a. the barbecue center of the West.

   b. a hot and dusty place to live.

   c. a confusing place to shop.

   d. an exciting place to visit.

C. Writing Practice

1. Select two of the "Words to Discuss" and write one sentence for each one. Use the same meanings as in the story. Underline the word.

   a. _____

   _____

   b. _____

   _____

2. Reread paragraph 2 of the story. Then write a paragraph explaining why Bernie consulted a map. Tell, also, whether or not you think that was a reasonable thing to do at the time.

   _____

   _____

   _____

   _____

   _____

3. Reread paragraphs 3 and 4. Then, describe Julie's behavior at the rodeo. In what way does she seem to be like or different from Sal?

   _____

   _____

   _____

   _____

   _____

   _____

   _____

4. Complete this analogy:

   Dallas Streets are to a **spider web** as **Philadelphia streets** are to a

   _____ .

Lesson 5: PRONOUNS AND THEIR ANTECEDENTS

Words to Discuss

spectacular	amphitheater	visibility
vista	rotate	creativity

What do pronouns mean?

Pronouns take the place of nouns. They usually refer to something previously stated, called the antecedent. In technical terms, the connection between a pronoun and its antecedent involves a relationship that requires inference. Examples: The man fell asleep in the chair because **he** was tired. (**He** refers to man.) The man fell asleep in the chair because **it** was comfortable. (**It** refers to chair.)

Preview the selection to get an overview of the main points. Then read the selection. Pay particular attention to the meaning of the pronouns you encounter.

The Scene in Denver, Colorado

Approaching Denver on I-70, the group "Fire and Ice" could see the mile-high skyline of the city. Beyond **it**, they stared at the *spectacular* backdrop of the Rocky Mountains, a *vista* that made the long drive worthwhile. The group drove along Valley Freeway and headed toward the Red Rocks Natural *Amphitheater*, where they were booked for their concert.

Red Rocks Amphitheater is an unusual sight. **It** was cut directly from the existing red rock of the mountain. **It** is circular like an old Greek amphitheater. Because the stage is in the center with the audience surrounding **it**, the group needed more time to set up for the concert. They had to make sure that they performed to the entire audience. The instruments needed to be *rotated* on the stage to give maximum *visibility* to everyone who was watching. Setting up on a round stage required more *creativity*.

The amphitheater is outdoors, so they were glad the night was clear and mild. The roar of the audience lasted far into the evening; their applause echoed against the rocks. Denver appreciated this music under the stars.

From Denver they traveled up into the Rockies to camp out for a few days. Snow-capped mountain tops were a surprise; they had seen nothing like this in England. Hiking around to look at the beautiful scenery, they spotted little flowers peeking their heads through the snow. Too soon, they had to leave the snow of the mountains behind them and return to the warm Denver sun. Then, it was westward again toward the end of their tour.

Unit 4: Inference

A. **Vocabulary Development**

      Locate the "Words to Discuss" printed in italics in the story. Read each of the sentences in which one of the words appears. Try to decide what the word means in that sentence. Discuss your ideas. Look the word up, if necessary.

B. **Are My Inferences Reasonable?** Circle the letter in front of the correct answer.

1. This passage is mainly about

    a. the long drive to the city of Denver.
    b. the unusual sight of the Red Rocks Natural Amphitheater.
    c. the snow-capped mountain tops in the Rockies.
    d. the problems and rewards of playing in Denver.

2. We can infer that the concert was a success because

    a. they played good music.   c. the weather was clear and mild.
    b. they played under the stars.   d. the audience applauded loudly.

3. From this story, we can infer that in England there are

    a. more beaches than mountains.
    b. many outstanding vistas.
    c. different flowers on the mountains.
    d. no snow-capped mountains.

4. This story suggests that in Denver

    a. the city may be warm while the mountains have snow.
    b. the weather is the same in the city and in the mountains.
    c. when the city is cold, the mountains may be warmer.
    d. both the city and the mountains are warmer than in Montana.

5. It seemed that the group would have liked to

    a. play more encores at the concert.
    b. take pictures of the spectacular scenery.
    c. play in an old Greek amphitheater.
    d. camp out for a few more days.

6. The vista that made the long ride worthwhile was

    a. the round amphitheater cut out of red rock.
    b. seeing the audience under the stars.
    c. the city skyline against the mountains.
    d. the city against the darkened sky.

C. **Writing Practice**

1. Select two of the "Words to Discuss" and write one sentence for each one. Use the same meanings as in the story. Underline the word.

   a. _____

   _____

   b. _____

   _____

2. Determine by inference which noun each boldfaced pronoun stands for. Underline the noun that is the antecedent.

   Example: Stay in the house. It is cooler **there. (There** means house.)

   a. Corey baked bread. **It** made good sandwiches.

   b. Mowing the lawn was difficult, but **it** had to be cut.

   c. Our neighbors next door are good sports. **They** are always willing to help out in a pinch.

   d. Newspapers bring bits of history and items of human interest into our houses every day. **They** are worth the investment.

   e. Many young people participate in sports. **They** build character as well as muscle.

3. Write two sets of sentences in which a pronoun refers back to a noun, as in the examples above. Underline the pronoun and the noun that is its antecedent in each set of sentences.

   a. _____

   _____

   _____

   b. _____

   _____

   _____

4. In the first two paragraphs of the story, the word **it** is used four times. Read each of the sentences containing this pronoun and tell which noun **it** refers to. Record the noun antecedents below.

Noun Antecedent	**Pronoun**
a. _____	Beyond **it**
b. _____	**It** was cut
c. _____	**It** is circular
d. _____	surrounding **it**

Lesson 6: CHECKING YOUR INFERENCE-SKILLS

Do I use inference skills?

Words to Discuss

smog	overwhelming	contagious
accessible	enthusiastic	procession

Check on your inference skills. Pretend that your shadow is watching you read. Put it to work to find out: Do you keep your mind on your reading? Do you use your experience background to help you make sense of what you read? Are your conclusions reasonable? Can you figure out what each pronoun means? Do you make reading make sense? If so, you must be using inference skills. Check yourself frequently.

Preview to get a quick idea of what the title means. Then read to find out why this trip for "Fire and Ice" turned out to be the tour of their dreams.

Los Angeles California: Concert Tour to Movie Contract

Los Angeles was shrouded in *smog* as the group approached it on I-10. This was their first experience with smog. Ghastly! However, the highway system was excellent; it made cities *accessible* and saved travel time. In England, highways are separated from the cities by winding country roads. "Fire and Ice" would miss the United States interstate system.

The motor coach stopped at the Los Angeles Memorial Sports Arena, a large sports and entertainment facility. Tonight they would be playing there, and it was time for rehearsal. The stage manager informed them that their concert was sold out. Hastening to the concert hall, they got directly to work on staging and lighting. They wanted to please the crowd. There was another reason why it was important

to put on an enthusiastic performance tonight. They had heard that a movie producer was coming to scout for a new film. This was their chance to be seen.

By show time there was a full house; that meant much excitement. The noise of the crowd was *overwhelming*, and the *enthusiasm* was *contagious*. With the confidence gained from their tour experiences, their performance was flawless. The producer came backstage after the show to talk about a contract. He asked them to stop by the studio the next day to sign it. A contract! This was it! They would be stars!

Their excitement knew no bounds. After a late dinner in Chinatown, they met a colorful *procession* going down the Street of the Golden Palace and joined in after the dragon. With joy they looked forward to the next few months in L.A. and then to returning home to recount their experiences to their families. From east coast to west coast, this was the tour of their dreams!

A. **Vocabulary Development**

Locate the "Words to Discuss" printed in italics in the story. Read each of the sentences in which one of the words appears. Try to decide what the word means in that sentence. Discuss your ideas. Look the word up, if necessary.

B. **Are My Inferences Reasonable?** Circle the letter in front of the correct answer.

1. From the passage we may conclude that

   a. the highways need repair.
   b. the winding roads are unpaved.
   c. England has no smog.
   d. Los Angeles and London are similar.

2. Traveling in England is _____ than traveling in the United States.

   a. more ghastly.
   b. more time-consuming.
   c. more costly.
   d. more interesting.

3. We can infer that the movie producer

   a. liked the group's performance.
   b. thought the performance was flawed.
   c. gained confidence from the tour.
   d. was confused by the noisy crowd.

4. The group joined the parade in Chinatown because

   a. it reminded them of home and family.
   b. they needed the exercise after dinner.
   c. they were excited and happy.
   d. they wanted a new experience.

5. They would tell their families about

   a. the overwhelming noise of the crowds.
   b. the distance between cities in America.
   c. the interesting foods they had tasted.
   d. their exciting experiences on the tour.

C. Writing Practice

1. Select two of the "Words to Discuss" and write one sentence for each one. Use the same meanings as in the story. Underline the word.

   a. _____

   _____

   b. _____

   _____

2. Keeping in mind the facts of the entire story and using ideas you have gained from other stories and from your own first-hand experiences, write a reasonable answer to the following question. What traits or characteristics did you notice about the members of "Fire and Ice" that might have led you to predict that they would succeed? Refer to the parts of the story that support your answers.

   _____

   _____

   _____

   _____

   _____

   _____

   _____

   _____

3. Write three to five sentences which answer the following question. Why did this turn out to be "the tour of their dreams" for "Fire and Ice"?

   _____

   _____

   _____

   _____

   _____

   _____

STUDENT CHECKLIST FOR UNIT 4

This checklist is to help you decide if your reading habits help you in making inferences.

Directions: Think about the following reading habits. Then put a check mark in the first column if you already have that habit. If you do not have that habit but plan to work on it, put a check in the second column.

	I have the habit.	I will work on it.
1. When I read, I put the facts together to come up with a reasonable explanation or conclusion.	_____	_____
2. I match the facts and details I read to my experiences to form reasonable inferences.	_____	_____
3. In reading, I know that not all of the author's ideas are stated. To get a complete picture, I must infer the missing information.	_____	_____
4. In reading, some ideas are implied or suggested. I can figure these out by creating a reasonable answer that accounts for all the facts.	_____	_____
5. When I read a pronoun, I figure out which noun it refers to.	_____	_____
6. I look for relationships between words or ideas to make reading make sense.	_____	_____

Unit 5: Understanding Visual Aids

INTRODUCTION

A visual aid is a graphic presentation of information. It is something a reader can look at to find information that would be more difficult to find or understand if it were described in words. In some respects, it is similar to an outline in that it presents important information briefly without the explanations found in sentences in the text.

What is a visual aid?

Sometimes visual aids are designed to be used along with printed information to make the text easier to understand. They are especially useful in explaining abstract concepts such as the effects of the jet stream on weather, which are more easily seen on a weather map, or the percentage of an annual budget spent on food, which would be easier to understand on a circle graph.

Visual aids present information so that we can see it and picture it in the mind. Whether used alone as a source of information or in combination with a printed explanation, the correct use of visual aids improves comprehension and increases the chance that we will remember the information.

Maps, tables, diagrams, and graphs are some of the common visual aids found in textbooks. Since they are expensive to produce, they are provided only for important information. Therefore, some attention should be given to them as they occur in the text.

Thought Questions

1. In the sentence, "A visual aid is a *graphic* presentation of information," the word *graphic* seems to describe something that is

   a. presented as a problem to be solved.

   b. clearly pictured as in a map or drawing.

   c. vividly colored to attract the reader's attention.

   d. rough in texture and irregular in form.

2. Four examples of visual aids found in texts are _____

   _____

Lesson 1: READING A ROAD MAP

What is a map?

A map is a *graphic* presentation of information about a land area. Not all the information about the land area is given on one map. There are many kinds of maps, each specializing in one or a few types of information; for example, a rainfall map, a political map, or a weather map. The map's *legend* is the key to the types of information given on the map. It tells what each *symbol*, line, color, or number stands for.

What is a road map?

A road map shows the state roads and *interstate* highways of a state, region, or country. The map usually indicates the mileage between *intersections* on the roads and between cities. A road map is used to find the best *route* to travel from one place to another or to find the distance between two points.

How does a map aid comprehension?

A map shows information about a land area on a small scale. For example, the United States may be shown on one page or less of a textbook. This allows the reader to picture the outline of the land as it would look from a high point in space. Seeing the land area all at once with the graphic symbols and lines that represent information about the land makes it easier to grasp and comprehend. Picturing it in the mind also aids memory.

How should a map be read?

In reading a map, first read the title. This gives the name of the land area shown on the map. It may also give other information about the area, such as "Rainfall Map of the Southeastern United States," or "Map of the Flume and Pool Areas of Franconia Notch State Park." Next read the legend which identifies the symbols and other markings used on the map. Think what it is you want to learn from the map. Then check the legend for the symbols, lines, or colors that show that information. You can then find it on the map. The legend is the key to reading the map.

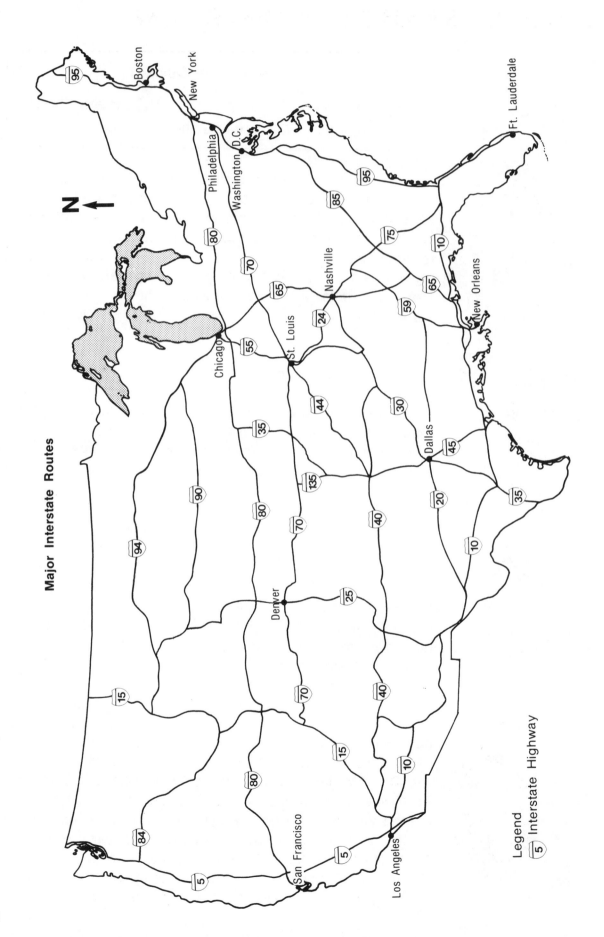

Major Interstate Routes

Legend
🛡 Interstate Highway

A. **Vocabulary Development**

   Locate the "Words to Discuss" printed in italics on page 65. Read each of the sentences in which one of the words appears. Try to decide what the word means in that sentence. Discuss your ideas. Look the word up, if necessary.

B. **Can I Read a Road Map?**

   Refer to the map on page 66 to answer each of the following questions. Circle the letter in front of the correct answer.

1. What route would you take from Chicago to New York?

   a. I-95.   c. I-55.

   b. I-80   d. I-70.

2. In what direction would you be traveling on a trip from New York to Boston?

   a. North.   c. East.

   b. Northeast.   d. Southwest.

3. In what general direction does the highway I-80 run?

   a. East-West.   c. Northeast-Southwest.

   b. North-South.   d. Northwest-Southeast.

4. It is farther from Chicago to New York than it is from

   a. Fort Lauderdale to Los Angeles.

   b. Chicago to San Francisco.

   c. St. Louis to Nashville.

   d. New Orleans to Boston.

5. A driver has a choice of routes from Denver to Los Angeles. One way is to follow I-70, I-15, and I-10. Another way is to follow

   a. I-25 and I-80.   c. I-25 and I-10.

   b. I-70, I-55, and I-20.   d. I-70, I-55, and I-80.

6. A city in the southeastern part of the United States is

   a. Boston.   c. Los Angeles.

   b. Dallas.   d. Fort Lauderdale.

C. Writing Practice

"Fire and Ice" visited 12 cities on their tour of the United States. They are: 1) New York, 2) Boston, 3) Philadelphia, 4) Washington, 5) Fort Lauderdale, 6) New Orleans, 7) Nashville, 8) Chicago, 9) St. Louis, 10) Dallas, 11) Denver, and 12) Los Angeles. On the lines below, write one sentence telling the routes you would follow to make each of the 11 trips. Use the map to find the best routes. The first one is done for you.

1. _*From New York to Boston I would take I-95.*_

2. _*From Boston to Philadelphia*_ _____

3. _____

4. _____

5. _____

6. _____

7. _____

8. _____

9. _____

10. _____

11. _____

Lesson 2: READING A STREET MAP

Words to Discuss	
vieux (*Fr.*, old)	alluvial
carré (*Fr.*, quarter)	descendants
Mississippi (*Algonquin*, *Missi Sipi*, Great River)	

What is a street map?

A street map is a map that shows the streets of a city or town and may also show transportation centers, government agencies, and public buildings. People who are not familiar with a city or town can use a street map to find their way around.

How can I tell directions on a map?

The directions *N*, *E*, *S*, and *W* for *north*, *east*, *south*, and *west* are often marked on a map with arrows. When they are not marked, we assume that up is north, down is south, to the right is east, and to the left is west. It is just as if you were facing north as you read the map. Sometimes only north is marked. We can figure the remaining directions from that.

The central New Orleans map in this lesson has the arrow for north pointing to the upper right side of the map. If you turn the map so that the arrow points straight up, you will be able to figure out the other directions. Keep this in mind as you study the map.

On the day "Fire and Ice" arrived in New Orleans, the group visited Preservation Hall in the old French Quarter, sometimes called the *Vieux Carré*. The next morning they took the St. Charles Avenue streetcar to do some sightseeing. Then they went on to the Superdome to rehearse. They must have had a street map to find their way around the city.

New Orleans is a lovely city to visit, a blend of the old and the new. It is situated at a bend in the *Mississippi* River on *alluvial* soil brought downstream by the river waters. The climate is pleasant, warm in summer and mild in winter. People from many European countries have settled there. However, the first settlers were French and Spanish. Their *descendants* today are called Creoles, known to visitors for their own Creole-style cooking.

A. Vocabulary Development

Locate the "Words to Discuss" printed in italics in the story. Read each of the sentences in which one of the words appears. Try to decide what the word means in that sentence. Discuss your ideas. Look the word up, if necessary.

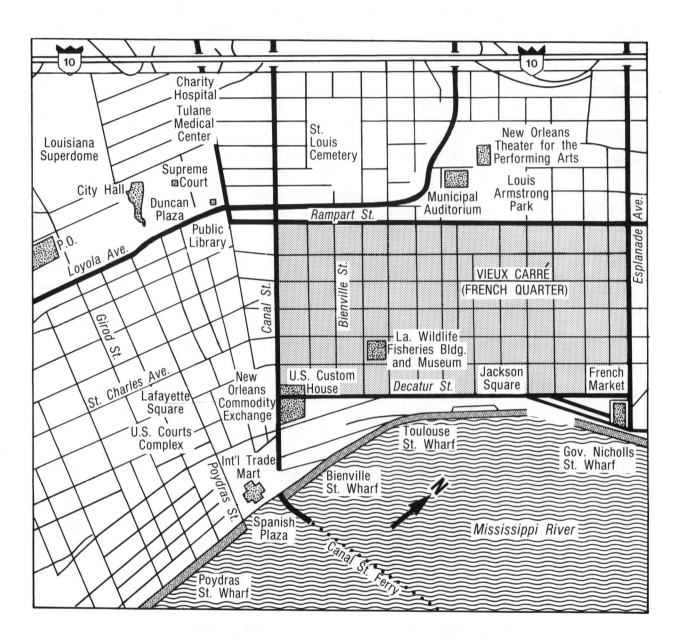

Map of Central New Orleans

B. **Can I read a street map?** Circle the letter in front of the correct answer.

1. In what direction would you have to walk to go from the Municipal Auditorium to the New Orleans Theater for the Performing Arts?

   a. North.   c. East.
   b. South.   d. West.

2. If you were on St. Charles Avenue and wanted to go to Loyola Avenue, you would have to go

   a. North.   c. East.
   b. South.   d. West.

3. In what direction is the Louisiana Superdome from the Supreme Court?

   a. Northwest.   c. Northeast.
   b. Southwest.   d. Southeast.

4. Which of these streets intersects with Canal Street?

   a. Esplanade Avenue.   c. Rampart Street.
   b. Poydras Street.   d. Bienville Street.

5. Which of the following places is located in the old French Quarter?

   a. Lafayette Square.
   b. Louis Armstrong Park.
   c. Duncan Plaza.
   d. Jackson Square.

6. The International Trade Mart is southeast of

   a. City Hall.
   b. Charity Hospital.
   c. U.S. Custom House.
   d. U.S. Courts Complex.

7. The Canal Street Ferry crosses the

   a. Pontchartrain Bridge.
   b. Mississippi River.
   c. Rivergate Exhibition Facility.
   d. Spanish Plaza.

C. Writing Practice

Give each answer in one or more complete sentences.

1. Give the names of the four streets that form the boundary of the *Vieux Carré*.

   _____

   _____

   _____

2. Name three of the wharfs along the river and give some reasonable examples of what these wharfs might be used for.

   _____

   _____

   _____

   _____

   _____

3. Find the Post Office (P.O.) on the map. Pretend that someone at the Public Library has asked you for directions to the Post Office. Write the directions that you would give.

   _____

   _____

   _____

4. Picture in your mind the route from school to your home. Now, write those directions as if you were telling a friend how to get to your home.

   _____

   _____

   _____

   _____

   _____

   _____

Lesson 3: READING A DIAGRAM

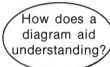

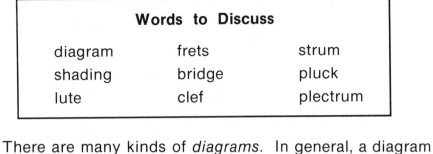

Words to Discuss

diagram	frets	strum
shading	bridge	pluck
lute	clef	plectrum

There are many kinds of *diagrams*. In general, a diagram is a drawing that shows the important parts of an object, such as a guitar or an insect; an event, such as an accident or the formation of groups for a parade; or a process, such as the growth of a seed or the steps in a science experiment. A diagram is usually done without *shading* or background to emphasize the shape or position of the component parts.

A diagram usually has labels on the parts, which aid in understanding and vocabulary development. In addition, diagrams sometimes summarize information that has been presented in the text; this is a useful way to review and clarify what has been read. A diagram may also be used simply to make information visual, especially when the description in the text is hard to visualize. Examples of this can be found in the instructions for assembling a bicycle or in a woodworking or auto mechanics manual. A knowledge of how to read diagrams has many uses.

Facts About the Guitar

For practice activities, this lesson features a diagram of a guitar. We should approach this activity with some background information about this popular instrument.

The guitar is a musical instrument in the *lute* family. It has a flat body with sides that curve in like a waistline, a round sound hole, and a neck with *frets* on it. Six strings are connected at the *bridge* and fastened to the tuning pegs at the top of the neck. The first three are usually gut or nylon and the remaining three metal. They are tuned low to high in pitch beginning with E below the bass *clef*, continuing with A, D, G, B, and ending with E, the first line on the treble clef. The player stops the strings with the left hand, usually, and *strums* or *plucks* with the right hand. A *plectrum*, or pick, is often used for this.

Although instruments like guitars have been played since ancient times, guitars similar to those available today were first used in Spain; they are still one of the most popular instruments of the Spanish people. They are often used along with tambourines and castanets to produce music that has great vitality and rhythm.

In this country, the use of the guitar by rock groups and folk singers makes it popular with people of all ages.

Ask someone you know who plays the guitar to tell you more about it.

Reading a Diagram of a Guitar

In reading a diagram, first read the title. That should tell you what the object, event, or process is. Then, look at the line drawing; observe each part with its label. When the labels are long or when the places that need to be labeled are too close together, numbers or letters may be used on the diagram with a key or legend (such as you would find on a map) to identify the parts. As you look at the parts and labels, think how they are related to the whole diagram. Keep in mind the text that you have read.

Diagram of a Guitar

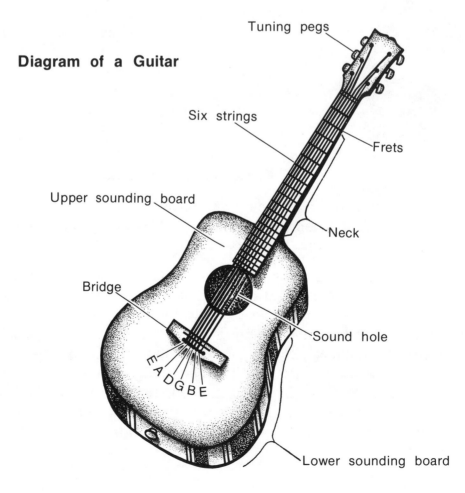

A. **Vocabulary Development**

Locate the "Words to Discuss" printed in italics in the lesson. Read each of the sentences in which one of the words appears. Try to decide what the word means in that sentence. Discuss your ideas. Look the word up, if necessary.

B. **Understanding a Diagram**

Refer to the diagram of the guitar to answer each of the following questions. Circle the letter in front of the correct answer.

1. How many strings are there on a guitar?

    a. 3.
    b. 4.
    c. 5.
    d. 6.

2. The strings are connected from the _____ to the _____.

    a. sound hole to neck.
    b. bridge to pegs.
    c. bridge to frets.
    d. pegs to frets.

3. Which is the longest part of the guitar?

    a. Bridge.
    b. Neck.
    c. Frets.
    d. Sounding board.

4. What is the order of the strings?

    a. A, E, D, G, B, E.
    b. E, A, D, G, E, B.
    c. E, A, D, G, B, E.
    d. E, B, G, D, A, E.

5. On what part of the guitar is the sound hole located?

    a. Upper sounding board.
    b. Neck.
    c. Lower sounding board.
    d. Bridge.

C. Writing Practice

1. Read the following description of a lute and study the diagram. Find as many ways as you can in which the lute is like or different from a guitar. Then, write one or more paragraphs comparing the two instruments.

Diagram of a Lute

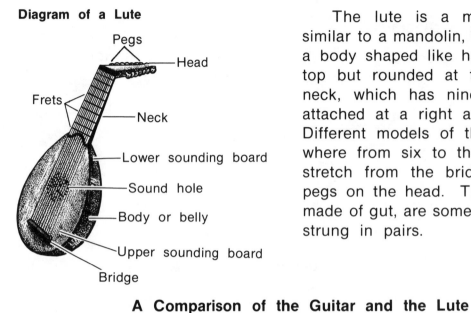

The lute is a musical instrument similar to a mandolin, only larger. It has a body shaped like half a pear, flat on top but rounded at the bottom. The neck, which has nine or ten frets, is attached at a right angle to the head. Different models of the lute have anywhere from six to thirteen strings that stretch from the bridge to the tuning pegs on the head. The strings, usually made of gut, are sometimes doubled and strung in pairs.

A Comparison of the Guitar and the Lute

_____

_____

_____

_____

_____

_____

2. Research the life and work of a guitarist of your choice. You may choose a classical guitarist such as Andres Segovia (born 1894) or a popular guitar player. Write a paragraph describing what you have found.

_____

_____

_____

_____

_____

_____

Lesson 4: READING A TABLE

What is a table?

Words to Discuss

column	data (pl. of datum)
row	statistic
intersect	footnote

A table is a display of information in *columns* and *rows*. The title gives the main idea, and the headings of the columns and rows tell what kinds of details are given. To find information, locate the correct column and row. The information will be where the column and row *intersect*. Study the two examples below.

Directions: To find the product of 8 × 3, follow down the column beginning with 8 and across the row beginning with 3. Where the column and row intersect, we find the answer, 24.

Use the table to find the product of 9 × 4. This is a very simple example, but all tables are read in the same way: by finding where a certain row and column intersect.

Multiplication Table

	1	2	3	4	5	6	7	8	9
1	1	2	3	4	5	6	7	8	9
2	2	4	6	8	10	12	14	16	18
3	3	6	9	12	15	18	21	24	27
4	4	8	12	16	20	24	28	32	36

The next table uses a combination of words (to name cities), numbers (to show temperature), and letters (to indicate weather); but it is read in the same way.

Temperature Range and Weather for Selected Cities on a Certain Day.			
	Lo	Hi	W*
Boston	55	70	R
Dallas	63	86	F
New Orleans	71	80	F
New York	63	79	R
St. Louis	60	70	SY
Philadelphia	56	80	R

*W — weather; F — fair; R — rain; SY — sunny

[1] National Weather Service statistics

The cities are listed down the left side. Three kinds of *data* are recorded for each city: the low temperature (Lo), the high temperature (Hi), and the weather (W). The asterisk (*) refers you down to the key to the abbreviations.

Each piece of data on the table is called a *statistic*. The source of the statistics is given in a *footnote* below the table.

Unit 5: Understanding Visual Aids

Practice Reading a Table

Use the Temperature and Weather table on page 77 to answer these questions.

1. What was the weather in St. Louis? _____

2. What was the high temperature in Dallas? _____

3. What was the low temperature in Philadelphia? _____

4. Name the cities where it rained. _____

_____

5. What does *SY* mean? _____

Reading a Population Table

Consider what the data on this next table mean.

Population of Cities on the Tour[1]

	City	Metropolitan Area*
New York	7,071,639	9,120,346
Boston	562,994	2,763,357
Philadelphia	1,688,210	4,716,818
Washington, D.C.	638,432	3,060,922
Fort Lauderdale	153,256	1,018,200
New Orleans	557,927	1,187,073
Nashville	455,651	850,505
Chicago	3,005,072	7,103,624
St. Louis	452,801	2,356,460
Dallas	904,570	3,974,805
Denver	492,686	1,620,902
Los Angeles	2,968,579	7,477,503

*The metropolitan area includes the city and the surrounding suburbs.

[1] *The World Almanac and Book of Facts 1985*; figures based on U.S. Bureau of the Census, 1980

A. **Vocabulary Development**

   Locate the "Words to Discuss" printed in italics in the lesson. Read each of the sentences in which one of the words appears. Try to decide what the word means in that sentence. Discuss your ideas. Look the word up, if necessary.

B. **Understanding the Population Table**

   Refer to the table on page 78. Circle the letter in front of the correct answer.

1. Which city has the largest population?

   a. Washington, D.C.   c. Philadelphia.
   b. Chicago.   d. New York.

2. Which is the only city with a smaller population in its metropolitan area than Fort Lauderdale?

   a. New Orleans.   c. Denver.
   b. Nashville.   d. St. Louis.

3. The population of the city of Chicago is larger than the population of the metropolitan area of

   a. New York.   c. Philadelphia.
   b. St. Louis.   d. Los Angeles.

4. The only metropolitan area that has a population smaller than one million is

   a. Nashville.   c. Boston.
   b. Denver.   d. Dallas.

5. Which city has the smallest population?

   a. Boston.   c. Fort Lauderdale.
   b. New Orleans.   d. Denver.

6. Which city has a population closest to that of Chicago?

   a. Washington, D.C.   c. Philadelphia.
   b. Dallas.   d. Los Angeles.

C. Writing Practice

Write one or more paragraphs in response to each of the four activities described below.

1. Describe the visual aid called a table. Tell what it is and how it should be read.

   _____

   _____

   _____

   _____

   _____

   _____

2. Study the Temperature Range and Weather table on page 77 and locate the six cities on the map on page 66. Then, write your impressions of the weather in the Northeast and in the central part of the United States on that day. Explain how you came to your conclusions.

   _____

   _____

   _____

   _____

   _____

3. The numbers found on tables are always in particular units of measurement. The units could be degrees, gallons, truck loads, cattle, or anything else that can be counted. What is the unit of measurement for the numbers on the population table? Explain how you came to that conclusion.

   _____

   _____

   _____

4. If 455,651 people live in the city of Nashville, how many people live in the suburbs? _____

   How did you find that answer? _____

   _____

   _____

   _____

Lesson 5: READING A BAR GRAPH

What is a bar graph?

How do I read a bar graph?

Words to Discuss		
graph	scale	axis
parallel	vertical	horizontal

A bar *graph* is a graph using *parallel* bars to show a comparison in sizes of things. A bar graph uses two *scales*: one on the *vertical axis* (the left side) and the other on the *horizontal* axis (across the bottom). One scale tells the size or amount. The other scale tells what the thing is.

In reading a bar graph, use the vertical scale to determine the value of each bar, according to its height. Think at what point on the scale a horizontal line would just touch the top of the bar. It is somewhat like reading a table in that we have to think where horizontal and vertical data intersect.

For example, think of two people you know who watch television. Graph the average number of hours per week each of them spends watching TV. Put yourself on the graph, too. You can do that by writing the initials of each of you on a line beneath one of the bars. Notice that the scale on the left goes from zero to 30+ (30 or more) hours per week. Someone by the name of Pat Doe is already on the graph. Use these directions to finish the graph.

Directions:

1. Put your initials and those of two others on the lines below the graph. (People in Sample)

2. Notice that Pat watches TV 15 hours per week. Find the average number you watch and make a bar the correct height.

3. Do the same for two others you know.

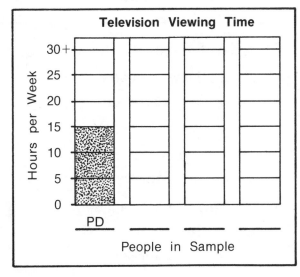

Television Viewing Time

Hours per Week

PD

People in Sample

1. Who comes the closest to watching 25 hours per week? _____

2. Does anyone watch more hours than you? ____   Who? _____

3. Does anyone watch 30+ hours? ____   Who? _____

4. Who watches the most TV? _____   the least TV? _____

Unit 5: Understanding Visual Aids

A. Vocabulary Development

Locate the "Words to Discuss" printed in italics in the lesson. Read each of the sentences in which one of the words appears. Try to decide what the word means in that sentence. Discuss your ideas. Look the word up, if necessary. Pay particular attention to the way these words relate to the graph you just completed. Be able to point out on the graph what each word means.

B. Understanding a Bar Graph

Study the following bar graph and then answer the questions below. Circle the letter in front of the correct answer.

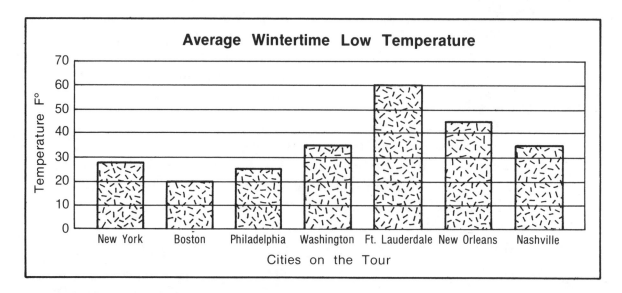

1. Which city is the warmest in winter?

   a. New Orleans.   c. Nashville.

   b. Ft. Lauderdale.   d. Washington, D.C.

2. How much colder is Nashville than New Orleans?

   a. 5 degrees.   c. 15 degrees.

   b. 10 degrees.   d. 20 degrees.

3. New York, Philadelphia, and Washington, D.C., are all warmer than

   a. Boston.   c. Ft. Lauderdale.

   b. New Orleans.   d. Nashville.

4. On the lines below, write the average wintertime low temperature for each city.

   a. New York _____   d. Washington _____   g. Nashville _____

   b. Boston _____   e. Ft. Lauderdale _____

   c. Philadelphia _____ f. New Orleans _____

C. Writing Practice

1. Write a one-sentence summary of the information shown on the graph, **Television Viewing Time**.

    _____

    _____

    _____

2. Write a one-sentence summary of the information shown on the graph, **Average Wintertime Low Temperature**.

    _____

    _____

    _____

3. Make a bar graph showing the height of each member of your family. The scale on the left goes from zero to seven feet. Keep in mind that each foot has twelve inches. Therefore, someone who is 5'8" would have a bar that reaches two-thirds of the distance between 5 and 6. (Eight is two-thirds of twelve.) Put the initials of family members across the bottom on the short lines.

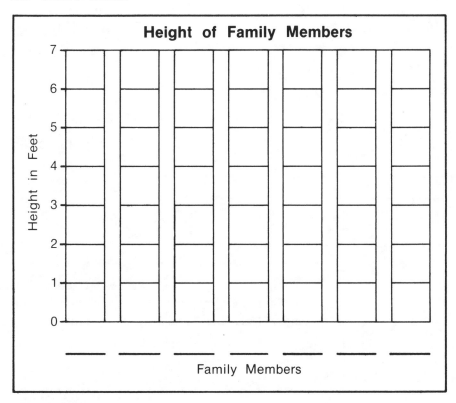

4. Write a one-sentence summary of the information shown on your graph.

    _____

    _____

Lesson 6: READING A LINE GRAPH

Words to Discuss	
process	value
plot	point

What is a line graph?

A line graph is a graph on which data are recorded by making a dot where the two values (row and column) for that data intersect. The dots are then connected by a line. The line emphasizes the changes in the data over a period of time or through the steps in a *process*. Each point that is *plotted* has a *value* on both the vertical and horizontal scales. To plot a *point*, it is necessary to find the correct value on each of the two scales and make a dot where the row and column intersect on the graph.

Practice Using a Line Graph

Pat took a math test every week for eight weeks during the first quarter of the year. Scores for the first six weeks are plotted on the graph. Complete the exercise to the right of the graph.

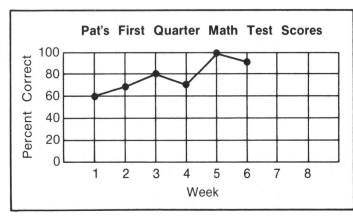

Pat's First Quarter Math Test Scores

1. Pat's scores for weeks 7 and 8 were **100** and **90**. Plot them on the graph and draw connecting lines.

2. During the quarter, did Pat's scores get better or worse?

   _____

3. Pat's average for the quarter is _____.

Reading a Line Graph

This line graph shows how the record sales of the group "Fire and Ice" changed over time.

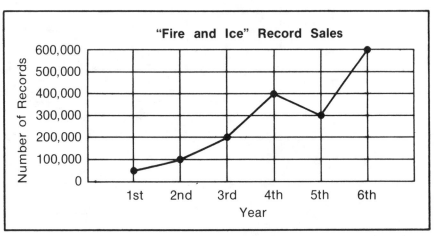

"Fire and Ice" Record Sales

A. **Vocabulary Development**

Locate the "Words to Discuss" printed in italics in the lesson. Read each of the sentences in which one of the words appears. Try to decide what the word means in that sentence. Discuss your ideas. Look the word up, if necessary.

B. **Understanding a Line Graph**   Circle the letter in front of the correct answer.

1. How many records did "Fire and Ice" sell during the second year?

   a. 100,000.
   b. 300,000.
   c. 200,000.
   d. 400,000.

2. During what year were the record sales the highest?

   a. Third year.
   b. Fourth year.
   c. Fifth year.
   d. Sixth year.

3. Record sales rose in every year except the

   a. first year.
   b. third year.
   c. fifth year.
   d. last year.

4. The largest increase in record sales occurred during the

   a. second year.
   b. fourth year.
   c. fifth year.
   d. last year.

5. The total number of "Fire and Ice" records sold is more than

   a. 500,000.
   b. 1,000,000.
   c. 2,000,000.
   d. 100,000.

C. **Writing Practice**

1. Write one sentence telling how many records "Fire and Ice" sold during their first year.

   _____

   _____

2. Pretend that you are one of the "Fire and Ice" group. You are in London, and the record sales for your fifth year have just been released. You all feel that you want to get away from the hustle and bustle of business to talk about the report. You pack a picnic lunch and take a cruise boat from Westminster Pier up the Thames River to Greenwich. You continue to the Royal Park near the National Maritime Museum. Basking in the sunshine, you all feel relaxed now and ready to talk.

   Write one or more paragraphs telling why the report made the group want to have this conversation. Mention some things that they might have said.

   _____

   _____

   _____

   _____

   _____

   _____

   _____

   _____

   _____

3. Make a graph similar to the one for Pat's First Quarter Math Test Scores. Choose a subject area in which you have received several grades. Put them in order, from the first to the last. Plot the scores on the graph. Then, connect them with lines. Title and label your graph on the lines.

What does your graph show?

_____

_____

_____

_____

_____

Lesson 7: READING A CIRCLE GRAPH

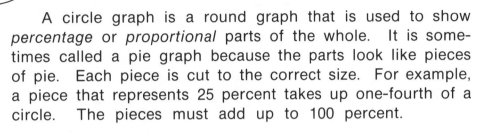

Words to Discuss

percentage   budget
proportional   assets

A circle graph is a round graph that is used to show *percentage* or *proportional* parts of the whole. It is sometimes called a pie graph because the parts look like pieces of pie. Each piece is cut to the correct size. For example, a piece that represents 25 percent takes up one-fourth of a circle. The pieces must add up to 100 percent.

This type of graph is useful in showing how people *budget* their money, spend their time, use their *assets*, or in any other situation where a whole of something is broken into its component parts.

Consider this example. In literature class students were figuring out what types of literature interested them and what percent of their reading time during the past year was devoted to each type. Fran came up with these estimates:

35% — science fiction (SF)

30% — adventure (Ad)

20% — biography (Bio)

10% — travel magazines (TM)

5% — poetry (P)

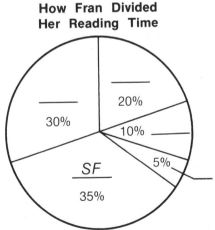

How Fran Divided Her Reading Time

Directions: Fill in the type of literature on each blank on the graph. *SF* is done for you.

Practice Reading a Circle Graph

1. Fran spends the largest percentage of time reading _____

2. Fran reads poetry about _____ percent of the time.

3. Half of Fran's reading time is spent on either _____
   or _____ .

4. TM stands for _____ , which Fran reads about
   _____ percent of the time.

Unit 5: Understanding Visual Aids

A. Vocabulary Development

Locate the "Words to Discuss" printed in italics in the lesson. Read each of the sentences in which one of the words appears. Try to decide what the word means in that sentence. Discuss your ideas. Look the word up, if necessary.

B. Understanding a Circle Graph

Study the following circle graph. Answer the questions below by circling the letter in front of the correct answer.

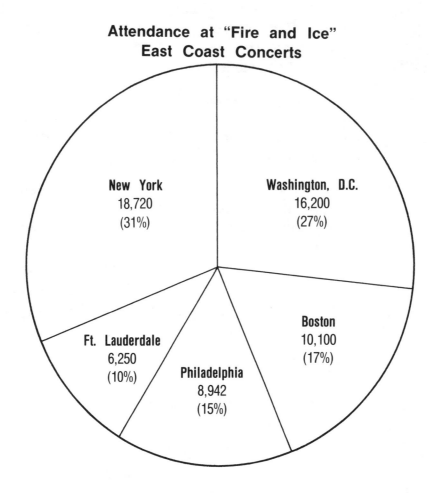

Attendance at "Fire and Ice" East Coast Concerts

New York 18,720 (31%)

Washington, D.C. 16,200 (27%)

Boston 10,100 (17%)

Philadelphia 8,942 (15%)

Ft. Lauderdale 6,250 (10%)

1. What is the total number of people who attended the "Fire and Ice" concerts in East Coast cities?

   a. 18,720.
   b. 16,200
   c. 60,212.
   d. 59,042.

2. In which city did the most people attend the concert?

   a. New York.
   b. Boston.
   c. Philadelphia.
   d. Washington, D.C.

3. In which two cities did the concerts attract more than one quarter of the total attendance?

   a. Washington and Philadelphia.   c. Washington and New York.
   b. New York and Boston.   d. Philadelphia and Boston.

4. In which city did the least number of people attend the concert?

   a. Washington.   c. Ft. Lauderdale.
   b. Philadelphia.   d. Boston.

5. In which city did the concert have less than half the attendance of the one in Washington, D.C.?

   a. New York.   c. Boston.
   b. Ft. Lauderdale.   d. Philadelphia.

C. Writing Practice

1. Think about the five cities represented on the circle graph on the preceding page. Consider the location of the city, the temperature, the weather, and the size of the crowd attending. Then, write a paragraph telling which concert you would have liked to attend and why.

   _____

   _____

   _____

   _____

   _____

   _____

2. Study the circle graph of Fran's Reading Interests on page 87. Think about the types of reading she chooses to do and what her interests might possibly tell about her personality and lifestyle. Then, write a paragraph telling why she might be an interesting person to know or to have as a classmate.

   _____

   _____

   _____

   _____

   _____

   _____

Lesson 8: COMPARING A BAR GRAPH AND A CIRCLE GRAPH

How are these graphs different?

Words to Discuss	
wedge	percentage

A bar graph uses parallel bars. Each bar tells the size, amount, or number of something. A circle graph uses *wedges*, like pieces of pie, to show the *percentage* or proportion of each thing to the whole. All the wedges must add up to 100 percent.

A. Vocabulary Development

Locate the "Words to Discuss" printed in italics in this lesson. Read the sentence in which the words appear. Try to decide what the word means in that sentence. Discuss your ideas. Look the word up, if necessary.

B. Understanding the Difference between a Bar Graph and a Circle Graph

The bar graph below tells how many records were sold in each of six states. The circle tells what percentage of the total record sales were sold in each state. Use the correct graph to answer the questions that follow.

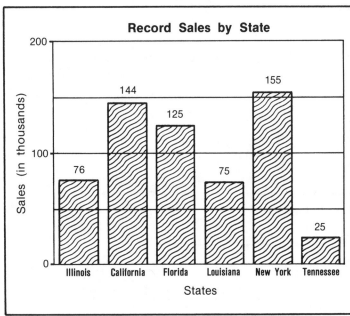

Bar Graph

Record Sales by State

Sales (in thousands)

Illinois 76, California 144, Florida 125, Louisiana 75, New York 155, Tennessee 25

States

Circle Graph

24.00%, 20.83%, 12.50%, 12.67%, 4.17%, 25.83%

Record Sales by State

Illinois, Louisiana, California, New York, Florida, Tennessee

1. Which graph shows how many records were sold in the state of New York?

   a. circle graph.

   b. bar graph.

   c. Both of them.

   d. Neither of them.

2. Which state had the largest percentage of record sales?

   a. California.

   b. Florida.

   c. New York.

   d. Illinois.

3. What percentage of record sales were in Florida?

   a. 24.00%.

   b. 12.50%

   c. 25.83%.

   d. 20.83%.

4. About how many more records were sold in New York than in Florida?

   a. 35 thousand.

   b. 30 thousand.

   c. 50 thousand.

   d. 80 thousand.

5. Which two states were closest in the number of records sold?

   a. Louisiana and Illinois.

   b. Florida and Tennessee.

   c. New York and California.

   d. Tennessee and Illinois.

C. Writing Activity

Write two sentences about each graph. Tell what kind of information is presented on the graph and what the graph shows.

Bar Graph: _____

_____

_____

Circle Graph: _____

_____

_____

Line Graph: _____

_____

_____

STUDENT CHECKLIST FOR UNIT 5

This checklist will enable you to decide if your reading habits help you when reading visual aids.

Directions: Think about the following reading habits. Then put a check mark in the first column if you already have that habit. If you do not have that habit but plan to work on it, put a check in the second column.

	I have the habit.	I will work on it.
1. I always read the title and the legend or key, if any, to a visual aid.	_____	_____
2. I skim the visual material before I read the questions that I must answer.	_____	_____
3. After I read the question, I go back to the visual material to find the correct answer.	_____	_____
4. I focus on the key words in each question so that I know what information I am looking for.	_____	_____
5. I always double-check my answers when working with visual aids.	_____	_____
6. I am able to close my eyes and visualize, or picture, the main features of the information shown on the map, diagram, table, or graph.	_____	_____

VOCABULARY REVIEW

The following words have been introduced as "Words to Discuss" at the beginning of each lesson. Read them through occasionally, choosing a few each time to add to your active vocabulary. Having a good vocabulary is an important step in improving comprehension.

purpose (Unit 1)
comprehension
contribute
alert
attraction
preview
advance
selection
destination (Unit 2)
international
ultimately
responsible
interrupted
board
passenger
assigned
taxi
beverage
attendant
descent
suspension
awe
massive
imposing
skyline
impressive
passport
efficient
borough
numerous
accustomed
amateur
impromptu
functioning
coup
simultaneously
crucial
acoustics
marquee

album
grueling
sequence
various
synchronizing
technicians
colonial (Unit 3)
conflict
massacre
staged
recreate
notorious
Parliament
independent
grid
sect
cuing
sub
capital
monument
striking
Capitol
complex
go-go
basking
reputation
capacity
receptive
encore
theme
deter
impact
trolley
hearty
Creole
specialty
rhinestone (Unit 4)
variety
interview

publicity
influence
devoted
pavilion
vivacious
financial
skyscraper
courtyard
vow
archway
soar
attraction
exposition
invention
accommodate
concentric
consult
snatch
shred
rustling
boast
spectacular
vista
amphitheater
rotate
visibility
creativity
smog
accessible
overwhelming
enthusiasm
contagious
procession
graphic (Unit 5)
legend
symbol
interstate
intersection
route

vieux
carré
Mississippi
alluvial
descendant
diagram
shading
lute
frets
bridge
clef
strum
pluck
plectrum
column
row
intersect
data
statistic
footnote
graph
parallel
scale
vertical
axis
horizontal
process
plot
value
point
percentage
proportional
budget
assets
wedge
percentage

ANSWERS

Page 6
B. 1. a 2. c
C. Answers will vary.

Page 8
B. 1. b 2. d 3. c
C. Answers will vary.

Page 9
Answers will vary.

Pages 11-12
B. 1. c 2. d 3. a 4. b 5. c
C. Answers will vary.

Pages 14-15
B. 1. d 2. d 3. c 4. b 5. c
C. 1. c, f, a, e, b, d
   2-3. Answers will vary.

Pages 17-18
B. 1. b 2. c 3. d
   4. c 5. a 6. b
C. 1. a. time, London, five, 7:30
      b. chicken, steak, steak
      c. sights, Statue, Liberty
      d. passport, customs, check
   2-3. Answers will vary.

Pages 20-21
B. 1. b 2. d 3. c
   4. a 5. d 6. b
C. 1-2. Answers will vary.
   3. Answers may vary.
      a. Both teams use a bat and a ball, are team sports, and have similar rules.
      b. Differences include the ball used, the number of players, and the size of the field.

Pages 23-24
B. 1. c 2. b 3. c
   4. a 5. b 6. d
C. 1. Map is given.
   2. Famous bands play there; indoor stadium seats 20,000 people; can hold 7 major events; and is the home of N.Y. Knicks and Rangers.
   3. Check acoustics, staging, and lighting; Julie checks vocals; Julie and Jeremy restage vocals; Dave and Sal tune instruments; and group practices their music.

Pages 26-27
B. 1. b 2. c 3. a 4. c 5. b
C. 1. Answers will vary.
   2. Answers may vary but could include the following: the group had to stand in a certain spot and sing directly into the microphone. When the sound was not clear, they had to record over again. Sometimes in recording over, they had to pick up the song in the middle or near the end. Each time they recorded over, they ran the risk of accidentally erasing the whole album.
   3-4. Answers will vary.

Page 28
Answers will vary.

Pages 30-31
B. 1. d 2. a 3. c 4. b 5. d
C. 1. Answers will vary.
   2. *Paragraph 1:* Due to modern super highways, the group arrived in Boston quickly.
      Paragraph 4: The group was excited about meeting some of the members of the Boston Pops.
   3. Answers will vary.

Pages 33-34
B. 1. c 2. b 3. a 4. a 5. d
C. 1. Answers will vary.
   2. The group was interested in the colonial days of Philadelphia and the music of the 60's.
   3. The group liked the music of the 60's and wanted to be as well known as some of the musical greats.
   4. *Paragraph 1:* Philadelphia was the first planned city.
      Paragraph 2: Philadelphia means "The City of Brotherly Love."
      Paragraph 3: The group was interested in the colonial days of Philadelphia and the music of the 60's.
      Paragraph 4: The group likes the music of the 60's and wanted to be as well known as some of these musical greats.
      Paragraph 5: Because there was no time for dinner, the group ate Philly subs.
      Paragraph 6: The concert scene was both exciting and draining.
   5. The group enjoyed the attractions and the people of Philadelphia.

Pages 36-37
B. 1. d 2. b 3. a 4. c 5. d
C. Answers will vary.

Pages 39-40
B. 1. a 2. c 3. d 4. c 5. c
C. 1. Answers will vary.
   2. *Paragraph 1:* Answer given.
   Paragraph 2:
   Main idea: The group had a chance to perform for the young people who buy records.
   Topic: Performing for Record Buyers
   Paragraph 3:
   Main idea: Although tickets were reasonably priced, the profits paid the group's expenses and their reputation was spreading.
   Topic: Expenses Paid and Reputation Growing
   Paragraph 4:
   Main idea: The group was very popular with the students who filled the music theater to capacity.
   Topic: Students Love "Fire and Ice."
   Paragraph 5:
   Main idea: The group was now ready to relax on the beach for a few days.
   Topic: Relaxation in Florida's Sun
   3. Main idea: Fort Lauderdale provided opportunities for success and relaxation.
   Topic: Success and Relaxation in Florida

Pages 42-43
B. 1. c 2. c 3. d 4. d 5. b
C. Answers will vary.

Page 44
Answers will vary.

Pages 46-47
B. 1. b 2. a 3. d 4. d 5. b
C. Answers will vary.

Pages 49-50
B. 1. a 2. c 3. c 4. a 5. b
C. Answers will vary.

Pages 52-53
B. 1. d 2. a 3. c
   4. d 5. b 6. c
C. 1-2. Answers will vary.
   3. a. New Orleans
      b. Washington, D.C.
      c. Philadelphia
      d. London
      e. Chicago
      f-g. Answers will vary.

Pages 55-56
B. 1. b 2. c 3. b
   4. b 5. c 6. d
C. 1. Answers will vary.
   2. Answers will vary but could include the following: The group was in an unfamiliar city; the streets in Dallas are hard to find; they did not want to be late for their first rodeo.
   3. Answers will vary.
   4. grid

Pages 58-59
B. 1. d 2. d 3. d
   4. a 5. d 6. c
C. 1. Answers will vary.
   2. a. bread   d. newspapers
      b. lawn   e. sports
      c. neighbors
   3. Answers will vary.
   4. a. skyline
      b. Red Rocks Amphitheater
      c. Red Rocks Amphitheater
      d. stage

Pages 61-62
B. 1. c 2. b 3. a 4. c 5. d
C. 1. Answers will vary.
   2. Answers may vary but should refer to the following: The group is talented; they work hard; they want to please; their concerts have been successful; they have had good opportunities.
   3. Answers will vary but should refer to the following: Their audiences are increasing; a movie producer was coming to scout for a new film; they were asked to sign a contract; they hoped to be stars.

Page 63
Answers will vary.

Page 64
1. b
2. maps, tables, diagrams, and graphs.

Pages 67-68
B. 1. b 2. b 3. a
   4. c 5. c 6. d
C. 1. I-95   3. I-95
   2. I-95   4. I-95
   5. I-95 and I-10 **or** I-75 and I-10
   6. I-59 and I-65
   7. I-65
   8. I-55
   9. I-55 and I-30 **or** I-44 and I-35
   10. I-35, I-135, and I-70
   11. I-70, I-15, and I-10; **or** I-25 and I-10; **or** I-25, I-40, I-15, and I-10
Note: Any one of the alternate routes is correct.

Pages 71-72
B. 1. a   2. d   3. b   4. c
   5. d   6. c   7. b
C. 1. Rampart, Esplanade, Decatur, and Canal
   2. Poydras St. Wharf, Bienville St. Wharf, Toulouse St. Wharf, the Gov. Nicholls St. Wharf (Any 3 are sufficient.)
      They may be used for tying up river barges, loading and unloading the barges, embarking and debarking passengers from cruise boats, and so on.
   3. From the Public Library, walk south on Loyola until you reach Girod Street. Make a right on Girod Street and walk one block. The Post Office will be on the left side of the street.
   4. Answers will vary.

Pages 75-76
B. 1. d   2. b   3. b   4. c   5. a
C. 1. Answers may vary but should include the following: The guitar is flat on the bottom and has a waistline in shape; the neck and head are straight; it has 6 strings, 3 gut and 3 metal.
      The lute is rounded on the bottom and is shaped like half a pear; the head is bent back at an angle; it has 6 to 13 strings, all gut, sometimes strung in pairs.
      The sound hole and the frets are similar on both instruments.
   2. Answers will vary.

Page 78
1. sunny
2. 86°
3. 56°
4. Boston, New York, Philadelphia
5. sunny

Pages 79-80
B. 1. d   2. b   3. b
   4. a   5. c   6. d
C. 1. See the first paragraph on page 77 for information.
   2. It was rainy in the Northeast and fair in the central part of the United States on that day. Data recorded on the table on page 77 show that the cities in the northeast reported rain.
   3. The unit of measurement for the population table is "people." The word *population* in the title means "the total number of people living in that area."
   4. The population of Nashville suburbs is 394,854. To find the answer, subtract the city population from the metropolitan population (850,505 − 455,651 = 394,854). Remember that the metropolitan area population is equal to the city population plus the population of the suburbs.

Page 81
Answers will vary.

Pages 82-83
B. 1. b   2. b   3. a
      a. 28°   e. 60°
      b. 20°   f. 45°
      c. 25°   g. 35°
      d. 35°
C. 1. It shows the average number of hours that Pat Doe, two of my friends, and I watch television.
   2. It shows the average of the daily low temperatures during the winter for seven cities in the eastern part of the United States.
   3. Graphs will vary.
   4. The graph shows the height of each member of my family. This type of graph is good for comparing heights.

Page 84
1. Plot scores for 100 and 90.
2. better
3. 82.5%

Pages 85-86
B. 1. a   2. d   3. c   4. d   5. b
C. 1. "Fire and Ice" sold 50,000 records during their first year.
   2. Answers may vary but should include the following: The report showed that record sales were 100,000 fewer than the previous year. The group probably wondered if their latest recordings were poor or whether they needed to do more promotional work.
   3. Answers will vary.

Page 87
1. science fiction
2. 5%
3. adventure or biography
4. travel magazines
5. 10%

Pages 88-89
B. 1. c   2. a   3. c   4. c   5. b
C. Answers will vary.

Page 91
B. 1. b   2. c   3. d   4. b   5. a
C. See the tops of pages 84 and 90 for information.

Page 92
Answers will vary.